Folk Songs of Australia

Folk Songs of Australia

AND THE MEN AND WOMEN WHO SANG THEM

John Meredith and Hugh Anderson

Ure Smith · Sydney · London

First published by
Ure Smith Pty Ltd, 155 Miller Street, North Sydney, N.S.W., 2060
London: Horwitz Group Books, 88 Farringdon Street, E.C.4

Published with the assistance of the Commonwealth Literary Fund
National Library of Australia registry No. Aus 67-936

Printed in Australia by Halstead Press, Sydney
Registered in Australia for transmission by post as a book

Acknowledgments

We wish to express our gratitude to all the people who assisted in the collection of the songs included in this book:

First, to the singers and musicians who gave so freely of their time and material;

Then to Sally and Fred Sloane, Joyce and Teddy Gibbons, Gladys, Arthur and Les Davis, Mr and Mrs Mick Brennan, and Hilda Lane, all of whom placed either their homes or their motor vehicles at John Meredith's disposal;

To Nancy Keesing, Professor Russel Ward, and Alan Scott, who made available material they had collected;

To the many interested persons who supplied the names and addresses of—and often personal introductions to—possible sources of songs;

To the editors and collectors of folk songs in Ireland, the U.S.A., and Great Britain, whose published works enabled us to make valuable comparisons and generally extend the scope of this book.

Without the help of these and other people this collection could never have been assembled.

The work of transcribing the texts and melodies from tape-recordings was carried out by John Meredith with the aid of a Commonwealth Literary Fund Fellowship. Since this book was written, the National Library of Australia has purchased the Meredith collection of tape-recordings as a 'notable addition to its Australian collection', and as a basis for a national collection of oral history. The following songs from the Meredith collection have previously been published in copyrighted arrangements by the publishers named:

Allan & Co., Melbourne: 'Waltzing Matilda'; and, in *Songs from the Bush*, 'Bold Jack Donahoe', 'Caledonia', 'Click go the

Shears', 'The Death of Ben Hall', 'The Eumerella Shore', 'Frank Gardiner', 'Jim Jones', 'Jog Along Till Shearing', 'My name is Dennis O'Reilly', and 'Widgeegowera Joe'.

Southern Music Publishing Co., Sydney: In *Authentic Australian Bush Ballads*, 'Australia's On the Wallaby', 'The Brokendown Squatter', 'The Bullockies' Ball', 'The Drover's Dream', 'Goondiwindi', 'Goorianawa', 'The Hut that's Upside Down', 'The Pommy's Lament', 'The Ryebuck Shearer', 'The Shearer's Dream', 'The Wonderful Crocodile', and 'Ye Sons of Australia'.

Finally, thanks are due to Angus & Robertson Ltd, Sydney, for permission to use Henry Lawson's 'Ballad of the Drover', 'Taking His Chance', and 'The Shearer's Dream' (all published in his *Poetical Works*), and A. B. Paterson's 'A Bushman's Song' (published in his *Collected Verse*).

Preface

The title of this book is a definite, though shorthand, description of its content.

Although the 1,200 items from which the selection was made were gathered almost entirely within the boundaries of New South Wales, the material presented is representative of the whole continent. *Folk Songs of Australia*, apart from being a unique treasury of all manifestations of popular culture in this country, is remarkable in that it does not attempt to draw the usual social and political distinctions implicit in the contemporary use of the term 'folk', and does not depend upon the printed word for the continuity of its material at any point.

The internationally known folk-song scholar A. L. Lloyd once wrote of English folk songs spreading two hundred miles in as many years, but the semi-nomadic existence of nineteenth-century bush workers in Australia spread songs, tales, and recitations over great distances in very short periods of time. The Sydney-side 'Bold Jack Donahoe' is collected in Perth, and northern Queensland's 'Australia's on the Wallaby' is frequently found in Victoria. Most of the songs included belong to no specific locality and the fact of their being collected in New South Wales is simply a coincidence of time, place, and persons. It is also probably true to state that no more than a handful of songs that originated elsewhere have not been commonly found in New South Wales.

At a time when folk songs are defined as songs sung by anyone calling himself a folk-singer, the authenticity of this collection must be emphasized. It does not belong to print and to literature, and the use of the word 'folk' in the title is not as a prefix of self-consciousness. The individual items vary from the smooth and relatively subtle to the coarse and awkward, but all

7

approximate the traditional and come as close as Australians ever may to music growing directly from the culture and work of an indigenous people. Each piece included, to some degree, fulfils the definition of John Meredith that a folk song is one composed to describe some happening or some aspect of the life of the singer, or of someone near to him, and 'written purely for the purpose of self-expression or commemoration'. For these reasons the compilers have been at some trouble to surround and enrich the items by extensively quoting reminiscences, by including details of source, and by introducing the necessary background material. In this way it is hoped that the songs will glitter like rough diamonds in a suitably natural setting.

Because of their concern for authenticity, the compilers have published only the bare melody line of the tunes, devoid of chord symbols. It was their aim to transcribe and present for students of folk song the melodies as they were originally played. They believe that a harmonic accompaniment represents only the way in which one musician would play the tune and that, particularly with modal tunes, it may destroy the essence of a folk melody. In his essay dealing with bush musical instruments (*The Violin, the Banjo & the Bones*), John Manifold dates the popularity of the banjo from the 1870s, but observes that 'only Will Lawson, E. J. Brady, and the anonymous author of "The Drover's Dream" appear to have noticed the instrument in their works'. The guitar is said by the same writer to have reached Australia as early as 1835, but, apart from one goldfields ballad, references to this instrument are rare 'because the guitar prefers the coast to the bush'. Of the hundreds of items forming the basis of this book not one tune was played upon nor a single song accompanied by a fretted instrument.

In a few instances, songs and dance tunes have been duplicated to demonstrate aspects of variation in folk song and music. From the examples given it is seen how a song learned from a single source by two or more singers can end by being sung to vastly differing tunes; and how a dance tune played by several musicians in the same district will develop many variations that may well be the result of the direct influence of the instrument upon which it is played.

What may be called folk songs proper, sentimental ballads,

and local parodies live in the minds of singers without prejudice. Most collections, however, limit their material to those items that have an Australian content or flavour and some look no farther than this single criterion. *Folk Songs of Australia* marks an important departure by including a number of songs of British and North American origin. The choice has been deliberately made since the compilers wished to cover all aspects of folk song *in* Australia, and to have excluded 'overseas' songs that have been handed on through several generations of Australian singers would have given a distorted picture. Some of these songs have acquired characteristics not to be found in the original song in its homeland and, indeed, there are some recorded here that are no longer found in their native country.

J.M. & H.A.

Contents

Introduction

Gathering songs in Australia
by John Meredith

I was only nine years old when my father died, but I have very clear memories of him. He was away droving sheep a lot of the time, out along the lower Darling River and on the Murrumbidgee, down Balranald way where he was born.

We kids always looked forward to his return from these droving trips. He brought us wonderful things from the far-away 'out west'—huge mussel shells from the western rivers, much bigger than we could find in the local dams; quandongs from which we would chew off the tart rind so as to get the round kernels, treasured because they made such beaut marbles; or some weird dried seed-cases of the 'devil's horns', that noxious weed that grows on the western plains.

It must have been tough on Mother when he was away on these trips because we were always hard up for money and she had to feed and clothe seven of us. But she always seemed to manage all right. We had an old cow and kept a few chooks and so were a bit better off than some other families in the township. It was usually bread and milk, or porridge and golden syrup—'cocky's joy', as we called it—for breakfast, and often bread and dripping or bread and syrup for dinner, but I don't think we ever really went hungry.

Mother had the knack of being able to turn an odd cup of flour and a bit of home-made plum jam into a tasty hot rolypoly pudding, usually singing to herself as she worked. She had a flat sort of singing voice, and didn't know many songs—I doubt if she knew any right through. Mostly she sang the beginning of 'The Wearing of the Green':

Oh, Paddy dear, and did you hear
The news that's going round?
The shamrock is by law forbid
To grow on Irish ground.
So take the shamrock from your hat
And throw it on the sod,
And, never fear, 'twill take root there
Though underfoot it's trod.

Now and then she would sing a fragment of 'The Shade of the Old Apple Tree', but, more often than not, if the song was not 'The Wearing of the Green' it would be 'Brian O'Lynn', and I always imagined from the way she sang it that it was all one word—'Brianolinn':

Oh, Brian O'Lynn had no britches to wear,
So he got him a sheepskin to make him a pair.
With the woolly side out and the leather side in,
'They're a wonderful fit,' said Brian O'Lynn.

I suppose it was while he was away on his droving trips that Father learned to play the button accordion, though I can never remember a time when he didn't play it. While he was away Mother would entertain us—and herself—in front of the log fire in the big wide fireplace at one end of the old kitchen at the back of the house. She would read to us from the *Australian Journal* or the *Bulletin*, usually episodes from *On Our Selection*, which was being serialized at that time, and a series about a funny character called Noonan.

During the periods when Father was home, in between droving trips, he would bring out the accordion after tea and we would sit around and listen to wonderful old tunes. The accordion was a 'Mezon Grand Organ', one of the old style with bronze reeds and in the key of A, these two features combining to give to the music a sad, haunting sort of quality. It was a bit of a wreck, but Dad always kept it in working order. The thumb strap was made from the tongue of an old boot, and the strap for the left hand from a strip of greenhide. The bellows were so patched up with bits of old cloth, stuck on with wattle-gum, that you could hardly see any of the original prettily coloured paper.

In front of the fire, Dad's face would take on that serious, far-away look of the button-accordion player, and he would coax tune after tune from the old instrument—things like 'Shamus O'Brien', 'Liza's Waltz', and 'Ring The Bell, Watchman', and a sad, haunting waltz tune that I carried around, half-remembered at the back of my mind, until one day, years later, Sally Sloane (one of the people from whom I was by that time collecting old bush songs and music) played the same tune, 'Jack's Waltz', and the memory of it and those nights in front of the fire came flooding back.

Another dance tune that Father used to play and that I have never forgotten was a very beautiful varsovienne—or, as most bush musicians call it, varsovienna. He could play the mouth-organ as well as the accordion, and generally used an old tin pannikin, held over the instrument, as an echo chamber, which made the music sound very sweet. One of his tricks was to play the mouthorgan and the bones simultaneously, which we always regarded as a wonderful feat.

After his death the old accordion was carefully preserved, and Mother would bring it out sometimes when we had a visitor who could play. Round about this time we made the acquaintance of a farming family, new to the district, who liked having parties, particularly 'surprise' parties. Sometimes we would be the victims of the 'surprise', and often would take part in giving other people parties. The new family's name was Wright, and 'Pop' Wright played the accordion well; I can still remember one of his set tunes for the lancers. Another family who joined in this party-giving was called Fields. The mother and one of the boys played the piano, and the other boy the fiddle. I remember they had the calls for the lancers written out and pasted on a bit of cardboard, which was always sitting on the mantelpiece ready for use, and so music and dancing were always a feature of these parties, although I don't remember anyone ever singing, apart from one chap who used to sneak out the back and blacken his face with burnt cork, dress up, and rush suddenly into the room to sing a nigger minstrel song. Dressing-up was a common joke at these parties. Usually one of the girls would dress up in one of the men's old working clothes, knock on the door and pretend she was an old swaggy looking for tucker. Sometimes the girl would almost carry the joke off to the extent of getting a hand-out, but usually she exploded into shrieks of laughter after frightening the daylights out of her mother or whoever went to the door.

When I was about fourteen my mother started trying to persuade me to learn the accordion. She would coax me to attempt different tunes on the old one, and finally held out the bribe of a new instrument if I learned to play the old one properly. I picked up enough tunes to qualify within six months and became the owner of a brand new 'Melba' button accordion. I could still remember some of Dad's old tunes; I learned more from 'Pop' Wright and from the Fields boys' playing, and then added to my repertoire with tunes picked up from visitors. A few other tunes I learned by listening to our old gramophone.

Later on, when I was about seventeen or eighteen, I would often be asked to bring my accordion to a local dance to play the 'extras'. These were the dances played by volunteer musicians while the hired pianist or band went to supper. Occasionally, when there was no pianist available, I would play for the entire dance, backed up by a drummer. This was more the exception than the rule, and it was a big occasion if I played for an entire night.

About this time I began to take an interest in Australian literature—possibly as a result of having been reared on *On Our Selection*—and began to read Paterson and Lawson. We had neighbours with a good library, and they didn't mind my borrowing their books. Then I bought a copy of Paterson's *Old Bush Songs*, brand new, at 2s. 9d. This was my introduction to the Australian bush ballad in its traditional form, but I rarely heard any of these ballads sung or recited until the revival of the 1950s got under way. I remember that a relation of the Wrights used to sing 'The Dying Stockman'. And we as kids used to recite a fragment of 'Five Miles from Gundagai' as a sort of bush 'toast'.

Folk songs of other countries always appealed to me, and when I came to live in Sydney I began writing down the words of some of them in a notebook, more as an aid to memory than with the idea of starting a collection. I still have that little book, which starts off with 'The Eriskay Love Lilt', 'The Skye Boat Song', and the Russian 'Sten'ka Razin' and 'The Red Safaran'.

I still had my old volume of *Old Bush Songs*, but it never occurred to me that the tunes for these songs might be found. I think it was the Vance Palmer–Margaret Sutherland volume (*Old Australian Bush Ballads*) which first made me think of the bush ballads as singing material. Even then I didn't think tunes would be found anywhere outside a library, and so I began searching in the Mitchell. Some of the songs in the old songbooks were headed 'Sung to the tune of such-and-such' and so I spent much time looking up old tunes to go with the songs; but as most of the tunes existed under several names, or had variants, I soon found that this method was far from satisfactory.

Hilda Lane, of North Sydney, first demonstrated the possibility of oral collecting when she told me that she knew an old shearer who still sang old bush songs. This was Jack 'Hoopiron' Lee, and as a result of meeting him and hearing him sing I bought a tape-recorder and began searching out old performers. Joe Cashmere was the next performer I visited, followed by Arthur Buchanan and Edwin Goodwin.

It was about this time that I had the idea of forming a small ensemble to sing the songs I had collected. Brian Loughlin and Jack Barrie readily agreed to be in such a group and we went into rehearsal. I played the bush accordion (or button accordion, as it is known in the trade), Brian the lagerphone, which we had met with during a holiday trip to Holbrook earlier in the year, and Jack the bush bass, a one-stringed, tea-chest affair which had been described to me by one of my workmates. We gave our first performance, more or less as a joke, dressed up in false whiskers and nineteenth-century clothes. It was a roaring success and we were invited to a social the following week; then to perform at a concert in the Rivoli Theatre at Hurstville. After much deliberation we chose a name, The Bushwhackers, then invited Chris Kempster, guitar, and Harry Kay junior, a mouth-organ player, to join us. Later we were joined by Alec Hood and Cecil Grivas, two vocalists who also played the bones and doubled on the bush bass or lagerphone when the occasion demanded.

The Bushwhackers' style and repertoire made them an immediate success and there were soon plenty of imitators. We secured radio engagements and finally went on some weekend tours. It was during these tours that I made many contacts for recording. When we performed at Newcastle, Lithgow and Mudgee we appealed to people who knew old ballads to get in touch with us. Soon, every weekend I could spare away from the band was spent in one of these towns with my tape-recorder and accordion.

Lots of people wanted to join The Bushwhackers, but we considered more than seven would make the group too unwieldy. Then somebody suggested a club, a sort of fan club, where we could teach our techniques and songs to others, with the aim of popularizing our native folk song. Thus the Bush Music Club, the first of its kind, came into existence. An attempt was made to establish an Australian Folk Lore Society, with the aim of encouraging the collection and study of oral material, but it became apparent after a couple of years that most people were interested just in learning to sing the songs for pleasure, rather than in studying their evolution and historical associations. Gradually interest waned in the society until, about 1958, it ceased to exist altogether.

When the Wattle Recording Company was formed (in 1955) it gave a further impetus to the work of collecting and popularizing folk song. Both The Bushwhackers' and Wattle's first disc was 'The Drover's Dream', recorded by the singer and collector of folk song Alan Scott. It was an immediate success: initially some two hundred discs were pressed; ultimately over 20,000 were sold.

I received further help from Nancy Keesing and Russel Ward at this time. Both were collecting texts of bush ballads, the former for the books entitled *Australian Bush Ballads* and *Old Bush Songs*, in which she collaborated with Douglas Stewart, and the latter as basic material for a doctoral thesis, published in 1958 as *The Australian Legend*. These two collectors frequently made contact with good performers and never failed to pass them on to me for recording, so that the tunes might be preserved. Thanks for their valuable help have been expressed in the Acknowledgments but I should like to repeat here my appreciation.

For a space of some four or five years I spent every available weekend (and every available spare quid) away with my recorder. Most of these trips were to Lithgow, Gulgong and, later on, Mudgee. When Sally Sloane moved to Teralba, near Lake Macquarie, many weekends were spent up north. I made several special trips, to places like Scone, Murrurundi, Holbrook, the Upper Murray, Beechworth and Albury, but nowhere did I meet with the success I did in the three towns west of the Blue Mountains, and I am convinced that there is still a wealth of traditional songs and music to be collected in the old goldfields area.

I seemed to be more successful than some collectors, and have often been asked how I manage to get on so well with the old hands. My plan, when recording, is to meet the old folk at their own level—to talk to them in their own language. It is of no use to tell them that you are a folk-lorist collecting folk song. They don't know the meaning of either word, and the use of polysyllables immediately classifies the collector as a city slicker.

I have always found that 'old bush songs' is a definition understood by most old folk; that a collector should always be prepared to sing a song or two and play some tunes himself to establish the necessary bond of sympathy with the performer. I often play some tapes before making recordings to show what other performers have sung for me, and usually demonstrate how the recorder works, particularly the ease with which unsatisfactory renditions may be erased. All this, in my opinion, helps to put the performer at ease, when a more natural performance will be given.

Frequently I have had to record wherever a power outlet was available, and often this was in a crowded pub or back-parlour bar. The crowd generally have collaborated by keeping silent during recordings, and often help with background data and the names of other performers, but I consider that the best method is to spend an afternoon or evening alone with the performer. Then it is easier to lead his or her mind back along the path of reminiscence and recollection without interruption from other people. I strongly recommend several visits to each performer where possible, even if only to re-record the items sung or played at the previous session. The chances are that extra verses will be remembered and most certainly interesting variants will be found.

Either in a notebook or on tape, along with the collected material, the collector should always record relevant details about the items and the performer. I neglected to do this in my early days of collecting, and many of the performers died before I could get these auxiliary notes. Things to note are:

1. The age of the performer.
2. Where born and reared.
3. Where items were learned;
   from whom;
   under what circumstances;
   at what approximate date;
   background of person from whom learned.
4. Brief family history.
5. Date actual recording was made.

If the amount of tape used is of no concern, all of this material can be recorded conversationally, along with any anecdotes the performer may recount. This is the technique I would recommend, as the performer will bring forth many interesting vernacular phrases which have passed out of usage, along with little rhymes and proverbs, all of which are worthy of preservation. One further word of advice to aspiring collectors: make a card index of your tapes, with cross references of singers and their songs, *as you go*. I let this work get behind, and it took many months of drudgery to complete the index for the collection of thirty rolls, each of 1,200 feet, twin-track tape, on which are over 1,000 items.

There are now quite a number of people collecting our heritage of folk lore with tape-recorders, but the number is not big enough. Every year the old performers grow fewer and fewer, and it is appalling to think of the amount of orally learned lore that these old hands carry with them to the grave. The collection of this material will only be done in this country by amateurs— by the time the libraries or universities get paid full-time collectors into the field there will be very little left for them to collect. Therefore I urge devotees of folk song to get out into the country with a recorder and gather the harvest before it is too late.

Part One
Songs collected
in and around Sydney

Jack Luscombe

When John Meredith recorded Jack Luscombe at Ryde in 1953 he was an old man of eighty-one years, but he was full of bright reminiscences of the life of a shearer during the last decades of the nineteenth century.

'There was a buggy-load of squatters,' Luscombe said when talking of the Shearers' Strike at Longreach in 1891, 'and we had pickets at one end of the bridge and the other, and let them get in on the centre, see; and we were going to take the winkers off the horse, and our organizer told us not to. And we let them come over and they read the Riot Act on one side of the river, and we were on the other side.

'He told them. He says, "Well," he says, "if you fetch your Gatling guns on," he says, "and start firing," he says, "there won't be a soldier left," he says. "We're well planted around like, you know."

'There was about two thousand rifles; there was twenty-three hundred of us. And our organizer—I just can't think of his name, but he turned crook; he turned conscriptionist over in Western Australia. But he did seven years.

'You see, we had a meeting at the hut before, it was about signing an agreement. That was the first agreement for the squatters. We pledged our word that we wouldn't go, but when we went up, there was one chap, he was going to sign, one that was with us, but he was shot. He never. That was the first agreement for the squatters. The P.A.U.

'Well, when the strike was on, things never turned out. We never shore; and they never give in. But our organizer, he got six or seven years, the ringleader, for it, but he was innocent. He stopped us from chucking them over into the river. There was no Gatling guns fired, only one revolver shot, but no one knew who shot the bloke that was there. One of the scabs. The bloke had given his word previous that he wouldn't sign the agreement. Well, when a man gives his word, he's not a man if he don't fulfil his agreement.

'Well, the next thing, we went to a shed, and there was a cook there—it was a scabs' shed—and he asked the heads like. He said, "What about cooking for them?" he said. They said, "What for?" And he said, "Well, I might be able to poison a few of them." And they let him go. And he had stuff in the blancmange, and there was only about thirty out of the seventy ate it. It made them sick and made himself sick—you see he had to taste a little of it. And, anyway, about two years after I met some of them, and they were still jumping then, their arms, after two years of it. He put something in it, all right.

'And at that time if you did anything that was crook they'd find out. Now I was at a shed and two Scotchmen we knew—they had done the scabbing, and we were at Jimmy Tyson's just over the border, there at Tinnenburra. And, as a rule, the first shed or two is not much good to you, because there is so many bagmen. It is better to be a bagman than to shear at the first shed.

'At any rate, these two Scotchmen, one chap knew them, and we had tea and they were sitting in. And so he gave the cook the office who they were. And he come around with soup, and instead of giving it to them—he had the soup in deep plates— he biffted them over the head with it. They was two brothers, and so the Representative, he got them by the ears and told them. He says, "You can't sit here"—and he put them out on the woodheap. Well, that's where they had their tucker for six or seven weeks, and if any other travellers or shearers would come along, like, they'd say, "Come out here and we'll show you a couple of pigeons we've got." Well, in seven or eight years they were the two staunchest men in the union. The best ever, like. You couldn't get better. But it took a while, like.'

In answer to Meredith's question regarding the origin of the word 'blackleg', Luscombe said, 'How did the the term blackleg arise? Well, years ago there was a disease called blackleg in the sheep. Well, in my time in Queensland, if you called a feller "scab", six months without the option of a fine. That's if you called them that straight out, but you could call them "Zambuk". That was all right, oh yes.'

Jack Luscombe spent his early youth in the Longreach district, and it was there that he learned his songs.

'I wasn't too old,' he said. 'I was eleven years old picking up. I started shearing at fifteen. I started in the sheds in '84. I was born in '73. I was fifteen when I started to shear. I was one of the first shearing with the machines. Yes. They had no universal joint or nothing then. They used to burn more guts on the inner side than they would shear. Oh, it was something terrible! It was like having one straight tube, you see—they hadn't that universal joint. You had to move the sheep around a lot. It's a lot different now. Oh, yes.'

The first song Luscombe recorded for John Meredith concerned a man's ambition to become a ryebuck shearer. (Ryebuck means expert; the term 'gun shearer' is used in the same sense.)

THE RYEBUCK SHEARER

There's a bloke on the board and I heard him say
I couldn't shear a hundred sheep a day,
But some fine day I'll show him the way,
And prove I'm a ryebuck shearer.

There's a bloke on the board and he's got a yeller gin,
He's got a long nose and he shaves on the chin,
And a voice like a billygoat shittin' on tin.
Of course he's a ryebuck shearer.

One song in the shearer's repertoire—'Click, Click, That's How the Shears Go'—is still chanted in some parts of western Victoria. The tune resembles Strauss's 'Trapeze Waltz' and there is also a similarity to 'The Man on the Flying Trapeze'.

CLICK, CLICK, THAT'S HOW THE SHEARS GO

You take off the belly-wool,
Clean out the crutch,
Go up the neck—
For the rules they are such.
You clean round the horns,
First shoulder go down,
One blow up the back
And you then turn around.

CHORUS:
        Click, click,
        That's how the shears go,
        Click, click,
        So awfully quick.
        You pull out a sheep,
        He'll give a kick,
        And still hear your shears going
        Click, click-click.

Like most old-time bush workers, Jack Luscombe carried his swag on the outback tracks. He told Meredith something of these experiences.

'When you'd be travelling you'd see all sorts carrying the swag,' he explained with a grin. 'But I shouldn't laugh. I didn't know how to roll it when I started out. And it was a bit long; it used to hit me on the hocks. I carried the swag at nine years old. But not far. Only about eight or ten mile. I was carrying water to ringbarkers. I was small, and the grass was so high they couldn't see me, but they'd see the grass waving and they'd know I was coming along with the drinks.'

Later, he tramped farther afield. 'Used to get along with the old corks on the hat. A billy of pups sometimes, you'd see the old fellers. And if you kicked a dog, you might as well have kicked the man. They'd shoot you. And they'd wear bowyangs. But people wouldn't believe you if you told them these things today. They haven't travelled. And you have to travel to broaden your mind and see how things is.'

One of his songs referred to a dream of Sir Samuel Griffith, Premier of Queensland and first Chief Justice of the High Court of Australia, travelling 'with a darky for a mate'. Griffith displaced the McIlwraith ministry in November 1883, and won the next election largely on his policy of preventing the importation of kanaka labour. Although the measure was inoperative, recruiting was brought under some control.

The villain of the song carried his swag in the New Zealand fashion—a 'collar-fashioned pack'.

SAM GRIFFITH

One night while lying in my bunk
In my humble six by eight,
I dreamt I saw Sam Griffith
With a darky for a mate.
I thought I met them travelling
On a dreary Queensland track,
And Sam was decorated with
A collar-fashioned pack.

I thought that it was summertime
And Sam had o'er his eyes
A little piece of muslin
To protect him from the flies.
Through his boots his toes were shining
And his feet looked very sore;
I knew his feet were blistered
From the Alberts that he wore.

When Sam saw me coming towards them
He sat down upon his swag.
Said he, 'Good morning, stranger.
Got much water in your bag?
We are victimized by squatters
For we are two union men.'
And Sam had on as usual
His same old polished grin.

Said I, 'Look here, Sammie Griffith,
You have a flamin' cheek!
If you want a drink of water,
You can get it from the creek.
As for the South Sea Islander,
I do not wish him ill,
For well I know, poor devil,
He is here against his will.

'You said with wife and family,
One time, you'd emigrate
If they did not stop kanakas—
That was in eighty-eight.
You spoke against black labour then
And talked of workers' rights.
You spoke from lips but not from heart,
Australia for the whites.

'You should loaf to those you crawl to,
The sugar-growing push,
For you're hated and detested
By the workers in the bush.
They might give you some easy billets,
Such as boots and shoes to clean,
Or driving the kanakas as
They work amongst the cane.'

I thought Sam jumped up,
Froth around his mouth like spray.
Said he, 'My agitator,
Just let me have a say.
I remember you at Longreach
How you did hoot and moan,
I believe you would have mobbed me
But for Constable Malone.'

I thought Sam tried to rush me
And shape before my face,
But I got home the La Blanche swing
And gave him coup-de-grace.
The darkie raised his tomahawk
And gave a savage scream,
Then all at once I wakened up,
And found it all a dream.

Luscombe had an interest in the nicknames of the people of the various Australian States, such as 'Gropers' for Western Australians. At one time he worked in that State.

'I shore in Western Australia for a few cockies, but they would only have a few hundred sheep. There was Jack Howe. You've heard of him? I picked up from him—in my days. He was a gun shearer. Three hundred and twenty-one he shore, with the blades, yes.

'This is only a yarn,' Luscombe warned Meredith, 'but I'm telling it as a yarn. Him and another big-gun shearer, they went up to a cocky's place. He said, "Looking for shearing?" They said, "Yes." They said, "Have you got any?" He said, "Yes." They says, "How many?" He says, "Five hundred." Howe says to his mate, he says, "You boil up the billy, and I'll cut them out, and we'll shift on in the afternoon." '

In common with many old folk who have travelled about the country, this ex-shearer had no real recollection of where he learned his songs, or from whom. He had picked them up in the different sheds. This was particularly so with his 'Kelly Song'. The one reference to Victorians in his reminiscences, apart from this song, was uncomplimentary. Victorians, apparently were notorious blacklegs. 'Why are two Victorians shaking hands like a lubra's [crutch]?' Luscombe asked. 'It is the meeting of two blacklegs!'

One day at his work John Meredith whistled the tune of Luscombe's 'Kelly Song'.

'That's "Just Before the Battle, Mother",' said one chap. A Baptist claimed it as one of his Church's hymn tunes, while a Dutchman insisted it was a Boer folk song from South Africa!

KELLY SONG

Farewell Dan and Edward Kelly,
Farewell Hart and Steve Byrne too,
With the poor your memory liveth,
Those who blame you are but few.

The final three words were *spoken*, in the manner common to quite a few of the older singers.

Ina Popplewell

The Sydney author Nancy Keesing discovered Ina Popplewell through the information of a Red Cross welfare worker who was helping the old lady.

In February 1954 John Meredith visited Mrs Popplewell in

the slum suburb of Darlington, an area in the South Sydney district off City Road which is marked down for clearance and use for extension of the University of Sydney. Nancy Keesing accompanied Meredith on his trip and has given permission to use the tape-recordings he made that morning.

They found Mrs Popplewell in a tiny old brick cottage in a back lane off a side street. The front gate was tied up with an old stocking—to keep out the local hoodlums, she said. Inside the cottage, although not very tidy, there was some lovely old cedar furniture. The sole source of power was a kerosene lamp.

The visitors discussed with Mrs Popplewell what they intended doing to overcome the lack of electric power for Meredith's recorder, and had almost settled on approaching the local publican for the use of a room with a power point, when Ina Popplewell thought of a neighbour who might have 'the electricity'. It turned out that she had, and she proved interested and co-operative.

Mrs Popplewell said she was seventy-five, but she looked older. She said she was born in Queanbeyan, where her father, 'who went as Collins', was a solicitor; he also owned various stations in the Monaro. According to the old lady, there was a remote family connection with the Macarthurs. She knew a great deal about the Monaro district, and it entered into several recitations that she said had been composed by her late father.

All of her material was received from her father. She had been conscious of the fact that he knew many ballads which had never been put down on paper, and had been deliberately learning them all from him, but before this was accomplished he had been killed in a fall from a tram when on the way to Kurnell to attend a ceremony commemorating Captain Cook's landing in Botany Bay.

'The Swagman's Joke' was recited by Mrs Popplewell, but may originally have been a song, for she added, 'I was learning that off Dad before he got too sick . . . oh, he knew a terrible lot of Irish songs, me father did; he could sing them, too.' The theme of the recitation is identical with that of 'Wild Rover No More', a song that appears several times later on in this book.

One of the old lady's songs concerned Frank Gardiner:

Frank Gardiner he is caught at last; he lies in Sydney jail,
For wounding Sergeant Middleton and robbed the Mudgee Mail,
For plundering of the gold escort, the Cargo Mail also,
And it was for gold he made so bold and not so long ago.

His daring deeds surprised them all throughout the Sydney land,
And on his friends he gave a call and quickly rose a band,
And fortune always favoured him until the time of late,
Until Ben Hall and Gilbert met with their dreadful fate.

Farewell, adieu, to outlawed Frank, he was the poor man's friend;
The Government has secured him, the laws he did offend.
He boldly stood his trial and answered in a breath,
'And do what you will, you can but kill; I have no fear of death.'

[Here the song becomes incoherent, as follows:]

Day after day they remanded him, escorted from the bar,
And from the cursed gallows this highwayman supreme—
He's doing two and thirty years, he's doomed to serve the Crown.
O'Meally has surrendered, Ben Hall's got his death wound,
Fresh charges brought against him from neighbours far and near
To prosecute this burgular was terror to the land.

And now it is all over, the sentence they are passed,
All thought to find a verdict of Guilty was his doom
And as for Johnny Gilbert, near Bendalong was found,
He was all alone and lost his horse; three troopers came in sight
And they fought the three most manfully, got slaughtered in the fight,
You may curse the day that you may say he met with Mrs Brown.

When she had sung the song Mrs Popplewell added softly,
'Mrs Brown shot herself when she found she couldn't get Gardiner . . . but Queen Victoria got him in the end.'

Except for a few metrical variations to fit odd lines of the text,
exactly the same tune is used in the song of 'Willie Reilly'.

The incident upon which that song is founded took place near
Bundoran in Donegal about 1745. The young Catholic Reilly, in
days when marriages between Catholic and Protestant were for-
bidden, ran off with Squire Folliard's daughter, a Protestant.
Joyce, in his *Old Irish Folk Music and Songs*, gives a song (p.
230) of fifteen stanzas besides a different air (p. 136).

WILLIE REILLY

'Oh, arise up, Willie Reilly, and come along with me,
For I mean to go with you and leave this country,
To leave my father's dwelling, his houses and free land.'
And away goes Willie Reilly and his dear Colleen Bawn.

They go by hills and mountains, and by yon lonesome plains,
Through shady groves and valleys, all dangerous to defray,
And her father followed after with a well-armed chosen band,
And it's taken was poor Reilly and his dear Colleen Bawn.

[2 lines missing]

It's home then she was taken and in her room bound,
Whilst poor Reilly all in Sligo jail lay on the stony ground.

Now Willie's dressed from top to toe all in a suit of green,
His hair hangs o'er his shoulders most glorious to be seen,
He's tall, straight and comely as any you can find,
He was fit for Folliard's daughter was she heiress to the Crown.

[3 lines missing]

If you have got them, Reilly, pray send . . . .

[2 lines missing]

And by his base contrivance this villain he has planned,
'If I don't get satisfaction, I'll quit this Irish land.'

Then out bespoke the noble judge, and at the table he stood by,
Saying, 'Gentlemen, consider, on this extremity,
To hang a man for love, 'tis a murder you must see,
So spare the life of Reilly, let him leave this country.'

31

'Good my lord, I gave them him as a token of true love,
And when we are a-parting, I will them all remove.
If you have got them, Reilly, pray send them home to me;
They are poor compared to that true heart which I have given to thee.

'There is a ring amongst them, allow yourself to wear,
With thirty locket diamonds all set in silver fair,
And as a true-love token wear it on your right hand,
That you may think on my broken heart when you're in a foreign land.'

Then out bespoke the noble judge, and at the table he stood by,
Saying, 'The lady's oath will clear you, or else will set you free,

[2 lines missing]

'Now in those cold, cold irons my hands and feet are bound,
I'm handcuffed like a murderer and tied unto the ground,
But all this toil and slavery I'm willing for to stand,
Still hoping to be secured by my dear Colleen Bawn.'

Then out bespoke the noble judge, saying, 'You may let the prisoner
            go—
The lady's oath has cleared him, the jury all may know;
She has released her own true love, she has renewed his name.
May her honour bright and high estate and offspring rise to fame.'

At the song's ending, Mrs Popplewell apologized. 'There was fourteen verses in it, but I forget. . . .'

Mrs Popplewell's memory failed her several times, besides which she had a most fanciful idea of a song's age. When she had sung 'As I Was A-Walking', for example, she said, 'That's a hundred and thirty years old, that one.' She also omitted several lines and added one or two from another ballad—a quite common occurrence.

'As I Was A-Walking' is a version of the Irish ballad usually known as 'The Mantle So Green'; in this book it may be compared with other variants sung by Mary Byrnes of Concord and Mrs Smeed of Mudgee. A different tune to much the same words appears in Colm O Lochlainn's *Irish Street Ballads*. His text is from a printed broadside, but the source of the tune is not disclosed.

32

As I was a-walking one morning in May,
For to view the fair fields and the meadows so gay,
I met a fair damsel, quite struck with surprise,
And I thought she was an angel that fell from the skies.

She had eyes like blue diamonds, she had cheeks like the rose,
She was one of the fairest that Nature composed.
And I says, 'My fair maid, will you come along with me?
We'll join hands in wedlock and it's married we'll be.'

'Young man,' she made answer, 'if me you'll excuse,
For my true love's in battle, I must you refuse.'
'I'll dress you in rich satin, you'll appear like a queen,
In your costly fine robes round your mantle so green.

'And here is the gold ring, he gave it to me,
Saying, "Take this, if you meet her, give this to Nancy."'
And she hung round by breast while the tears down did flow,
[Line missing]

Here's luck to all Mothers, and those rears a son,
And you don't know the hardships that poor Peter run,
Locked up in cold barracks all night and next day—
He ne'er would have 'listed or wore the cockade.

If my father had been a wise man and learned me some trade,
I ne'er would have 'listed or wore the cockade.
[2 lines missing]

Mrs Popplewell told John Meredith that her father sang 'The Battle Cry of Freedom' and played the tune on his concertina. 'It was beautiful, too,' she said. There was a song of this name, words and music by G. F. Root, which was widely published in American community songbooks of the 1920s. It probably derived from the Vaterlandslied 'Der Gott, der Eisen wachsen liess', the music of which was written by A. G. Methfessel to words by E. M. Arndt.

C

How the darkies gobbled when they heard the distant sound,
And how the new potatoes they kept sprouting through the ground.
And now we'll sing the chorus from the land unto the sea,
Shouting the battle cry of freedom!

CHORUS:

 Hurrah! Hurrah! We'll sound the jubilee.
 Hurrah! Hurrah! For the flag that sets us free.
 And now we'll sing the chorus from the land unto the sea.
 Shouting the battle cry of freedom!

The Union for ever then, hurrah, boys, hurrah!
We will up with the traitor and down with the star,
And we'll rally from the inside and we'll rally from the out,
Shouting the battle cry of freedom.

There are few folk songs about the city extant. Most that have been collected probably had their origin in either the music halls or the peddled broadside. A few of the well-known street and pub singers, such as Blind Billy Huntington, may have composed ballads on local events and characters. Two city songs that Ina Popplewell recorded were 'Sydney Cup Day' and 'Take Me Down the Harbour'. The latter was a music-hall ditty that was very popular in Sydney at the turn of the century. Dozens of old people still sing the song today.

SYDNEY CUP DAY

It was on a Sydney Cup Day,
While strolling round the course,
Joe Thompson he came up to me
And said, 'Will you back my horse?
And if you wish to back one,
You see there's three to one . . .'
[2 lines missing]

You may be very tricky
And you may be very sly;
You can always find your match
If you only like to try.
And what you do is clever—
On that we all agree.
You may have got at one or two
But you won't get at me.

TAKE ME DOWN THE HARBOUR

Take me down the Harbour on a Sunday afternoon,
To Manly Beach or Watson's Bay
Or round to Coogee for a day.
Call around at Clifton, or Mosman, it will do;
Good old Harbour, Sydney Town,
They can't beat you.

Way over the tide, how softly they glide,
Out on the Harbour ferry.
If you feel alone, ring me up on the 'phone,
You're just the girl I'm needing.

Take me down the Harbour on a Sunday afternoon,
To Manly Beach or Watson's Bay
Or round to Coogee for a day.
Call around at Clifton, or Mosman, it will do;
Good old Harbour, Sydney Town,
They can't beat you.

Included in Mrs Popplewell's repertoire were several popular songs, mostly of music-hall origin, that had been learned and stored away in memory and finally recorded almost unchanged. The usual tendency was to shorten the songs. This is exemplified in her version of 'Botany Bay'.

BOTANY BAY

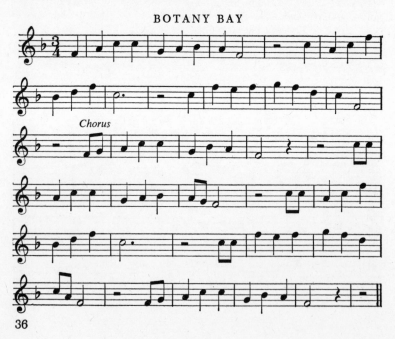

> *Farewell to old England for ever,*
> *Farewell to its rumkulls as well.*
> *Farewell to the well-known Old Bailey,*
> *Where we used for to cut such a swell.*

CHORUS:
> *Singing tooral-i-ooral-i-addiday,*
> *Singing tooral-i-ooral-i-ay,*
> *Singing tooral-i-ooral-i-addiday,*
> *Singing tooral-i-ooral-i-ay.*

> *There's the Captain as all us commands,*
> *There's the bos'n and all the ship's crew,*
> *There's the first- and the second-class passengers—*
> *Know what we poor convicts go through.*

> *If I had the wings of a turtle-dove*
> *I'd soar on my pinions so high,*
> *Right into the arms of my Polly love,*
> *And there I would stay till I died.*

Although Mrs Popplewell claimed of 'Botany Bay', 'That's old, that's a hundred years old too, that's a very old one—I learned that off me father', it is probable that he learned it in the 1890s. This song is probably the best known of those so named and was popular at the turn of the century among folk-singers in England. Quite a number of versions have appeared in print, including one in *The Sydney Golden Songster* (1893), entitled 'Too-Ral, Li-Ooral, Li-Additty'.

Jack ('Hoopiron') Lee

Hilda Lane discovered Jack Lee when she assisted the old man, blind and tapping his way, into North Sydney station. The two talked for a while. Hilda found that he knew and sang old bush songs and later introduced him to Russel Ward, who was at that time collecting material for the thesis since published as *The Australian Legend*.

John Meredith, together with Chris Kempster, was invited over to Mrs Lane's flat the following Sunday afternoon to listen to the old chap sing and take down some of his songs.

They took the entire afternoon to write down the music of one verse of 'The Backblock Shearer' and soon realized what a marathon task lay ahead of them in transcribing the complete list of Jack Lee's songs. Meredith made an appointment with 'Hoop-iron' for the next Sunday and went off to borrow a tape-recorder. In a few hours he had taped the singer's repertoire as well as that of his younger brother, Colin (p. 47), who played the button accordion.

THE BACKBLOCK SHEARER

I'm only a backblock shearer,
As easily can be seen;
I've shorn in most of the sheds
On the plains of the Riverine.
I've shorn in most of the famous sheds,
I've seen big tallies done,
But somehow or other, I don't know why,
I never became a gun.

CHORUS:
    Hurrah! my boys, my shears are set,
    I feel both fit and well;
    Tomorrow you'll find me at my pen
    When the gaffer rings the bell.
    With Hayden's patent thumb guards fixed
    And both my blades pulled back,
    Tomorrow I go with my sardine blow
    For a century or the sack.

I've opened up the windpipe straight,
I've opened behind the ear,
I've practised all the possible styles
In which a man can shear.

I've studied all the cuts and drives
Of the famous men I've met,
But I've never succeeded in plastering up
Those three little figures yet.

When the boss walked down the board this morning
He stopped and stared at me,
For I'd mastered Moran's great shoulder cut,
As he could plainly see.
But I've another surprise for him
That will give his nerves a shock:
Tomorrow I'll show him I have mastered
Pierce's rang-tang block.

And if I succeed as I expect to do,
Next year I intend to shear
At the Wagga demonstration
That is held there every year.
And there I'll lower the colours,
The colours of Mitchell & Co.,
Instead of Deeming you will hear
Of Widgeegowera Joe.

'Twas in the old shed at Coorong
Where I first flashed a blade,
But now the years have vanished
Along with the cheques that I've made.
[The rest of this verse missing]

Jack Lee always finished that song with an enthusiastic
'Whacko!' He said that he once shore at a shed called Nimidgee,
near Mount Hope, in New South Wales, where almost everyone was a singer and joined in the nightly singsongs. Amongst
the shearers was Bill Tully, who wrote the words of 'The Backblock Shearer' at the time. Tully was the author of 'Silver
Cheques', verses printed in the *Bulletin* of 19th November 1903,
and reprinted in Pizer's *Freedom on the Wallaby*. These verses
may be compared with the song, which, incidentally, originally
had slightly different wording for the first half of the last verse:

'Twas in the old shed at Tarwong
Where first I flashed a blade,
But now the years have vanished along
With the cheques that I have made.

The tune for 'The Backblock Shearer' is a variant of that for an Irish transportation ballad called 'Castle Gardens' (p. 54).

After his one experience of trying to take down musical notation accurately, Meredith sold his prized camera to raise the deposit on a tape-recorder of his own. Unfortunately, he was new to the techniques needed and succeeded in erasing the entire Lee recording of the previous week. All that remained was a few typed texts and one or two transcribed tunes. Back he went to Jack Lee.

Poor old Jack was suffering from an attack of bronchitis and could not sing his best, but Colin, thrilled with the novelty of the recorder, had invited several friends and relations in to see the modern marvel. Apart from persuading a reluctant Jackie Lee to sing, John had to cope with a roomful of people bent on holding a 'recorder party'.

Jack Lee sang at least a verse and the chorus of most of his songs on that occasion. John Meredith was thankful he had managed to retrieve most of what he had previously lost through inexperience, for shortly afterwards 'Hoopiron' died.

After Jack had sung 'The Old Man Kangaroo', Colin gave his own version of the tune on the accordion.

THE OLD MAN KANGAROO

Bill Chippen and myself got bushed out in a mallee scrub,
For three long days and three long nights without a taste of grub;
And on the third, my bonny word, my word, I tell you true,
When Bill espied with joyful pride an old man kangaroo.

That kangaroo he sighted us and sat upon his tail,
And as we approached him did neither flinch nor quail.
He seemed to say, 'Just step this way. What business, friend, have
    you?'
'By jove,' said Bill, 'I'd like to kill that old man kangaroo.'

Bill walked toward the hairy brute, a cudgel in his hand,
Walked up to the kangaroo, who defiantly did stand.
He made a blow at the hairy foe, the foe, I tell you true,
He grabbed my mate, as sure as fate, did the old man kangaroo.

Then he grabbed my mate around the waist, which made poor
    William bawl,
'Oh, come hither quick and bring a stick—he'll bust me with a fall.
He has me in his tight embrace, by jove, I tell you true,
Come hither quick and bring a stick and kill the kangaroo.'

A lucky thought came in my head to set poor William free—
The bump of agility is very big with me—
So from my swag my tucker-bag, provisionless, I drew;
I ran to where Bill in despair tugged with the kangaroo.

And stealing up behind the beast, the bag I opened wide;
I slipped it right down o'er his head, and then the string I tied
Around his neck. It seemed to check his progress, so I drew
My dover out and with a shout I tailed the kangaroo.

A kangaroo without a tail can't hop, of course, you know,
And finding his appendage gone he let poor William go.
He gave a wail for the hairy tail, the tale I tell you true,
He gave a jump and sank a lump of lifeless kangaroo.

My mate was not much knocked about, and scarcely was he freed,
'By jove,' said Bill, 'I think it's time that we did have a feed.'
So Bill he got the billy-pot, he made a splendid stew,
And the sweetest meat I ever eat was the tail of that kangaroo.

Colin Lee's version of the tune:

Jack Lee was seventy-seven when Meredith recorded his songs and had been blind for a number of years. Born in Booligal in 1876, he spent his later years in Auburn, a Sydney suburb, where he lived with his sister and brother. The nickname 'Hoopiron' was bestowed because of his ability to adapt that commodity to so many uses—making handles for golden-syrup tins to convert them into pint-pots, or repairing chairs, tables, and fences.

Lee remembered a couple of lines of some Ned Kelly songs, but said they were regarded as 'treason songs' in his younger days, and that policemen stopped men from singing them. He also recited a 'toast':

> *I've roped the green-eyed stag,*
> *And cracked the greenhide whip.*
> *I'll bid farewell to Cunnamulla*
> *And do another trip.*

These bush toasts were usually, as here, a quatrain in length. Quite often they became a standing joke in a pub, one drinker reciting the first line and then pausing for someone else to join in with the remainder.

THE BROKEN-DOWN SQUATTER

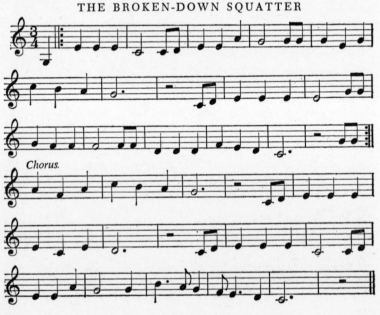

Come, Stumpy, old man, we must shift while we can;
All your mates in the paddock are dead.
Let us bid our farewells to Glen Eva's sweet dells
And the place where your master was bred;
Together we'll roam from our drought-stricken home—
It seems hard that such things have to be.
And it's hard on a horse when he's nought for a boss
But a broken-down squatter like me.

CHORUS:
For the banks are all broken, they say,
And the merchants are all up a tree.
When the bigwigs are brought to the Bankruptcy Court,
What chance for a squatter like me?

No more shall we muster the river for fats,
Or spiel on the Fifteen Mile Plain,
Or rip through the scrub by the light of the moon
Or see the old stockyard again.
Leave the slip panels down, it won't matter much now,
There are none but the crows left to see,
Perching gaunt on yon pine, as though longing to dine
On a broken-down squatter like me.

When the country was cursed with the drought at its worst
And the cattle were dying in scores,
Though down on my luck I kept up my pluck,
Thinking justice might temper the laws.
But the farce has been played and the government aid
Ain't extended to squatters, old son.
When my money was spent they doubled the rent,
And resumed the best half of the run.

'Twas done without reason, for, leaving the season,
No squatter could stand such a rub;
For it's useless to squat when the rents are so hot
That you can't save the price of your grub.
And there's not much to choose 'twixt the banks and the Jews
Once a fellow gets put up a tree.
No odds what I feel, there's no court of appeal
For a broken-down squatter like me.

This song, no doubt, came into being between 1891, when the squatters were at war with the Shearers' Union in an endeavour to reduce the rate of payment, and 1893, when the banks crashed. Prior to this period, for at least a decade, both bush workers and their employers had enjoyed good times.

One unusual song—in the sense that it is rarely sung—recorded from Jack Lee's singing was 'The Maid and the Magpie'.

THE MAID AND THE MAGPIE

Once there was a maid who kept an old magpie.
A parson in a church used to preach close by.
Her lover was a sailor, he sailed upon the main;
She promised she would be his wife when he returned again.
But still she let that parson see her home from church;
She was never thinking of the magpie on the perch.

CHORUS:

    The maid and the magpie would chatter all the day,
    The maid would believe what the magpie would say.
    She said she loved the parson—'But don't you tell the tar!'
    The knowing old bird only said 'Kwah-kwah!'

She said unto the magpie, while talking to him one day,
'I'd rather have the parson now the sailor is away;
I meet the parson every night at nine down near the church,
But if you tell the secret, why, I'll give you the birch.'
The knowing old bird only 'kwah-kwahed' as he had done before;
Still, he meant to tell the secret when Jack returned on shore.

While stationed at Gibraltar, the sailor, so it seems,
While sleeping in his cosy bunk, he had some funny dreams.
The girl he left behind him on dear old Aussie's shore,
He dreamt no doubt that she might flirt with half a dozen more.
So he made his passage homeward as quickly as could be.
Going to the maiden's house, no maiden could he see;
He then went to the old magpie, who was hopping on his perch,
And he told him all about it—the parson and the church.

When Jack met the maiden he passed her with disdain;
She sued for breach of promise, tried five hundred pounds to gain,
But he took the magpie into court, who told the truthful tale;
To get what she required the maiden she did fail.
She went out for the parson but in vain for him did search—
He knew which way the wind blew and hooked it from the church.
The lawyers tried to find him out but the case went on the shelf,
And the tricky little damsel had to live by herself.

LAST CHORUS:
The maid and the magpie didn't chatter all the day;
The jolly little sailor boy took the knowing bird away,
And while to his shipmates the right good-hearted tar
Is telling them his tale of love, the old bird sings 'Kwah-kwah!'

Jack Lee suggested that Meredith call on Joe Cashmere, his
old mate from Booligal, who was a singer of some renown as
well as being able to play the fiddle. When Cashmere heard the
tape-recording of Lee singing 'The Old Jig-jog' (Paterson's 'A
Bushman's Song') he chuckled and said, 'Poor old Jacky, he's
certainly forgotten that tune', and went on to sing his own version, a variant of the same tune (see p. 83). Lee's version follows.

THE OLD JIG-JOG

I'm travelling down the Castlereagh, and I'm a station-hand,
I'm handy with the roping pole, I'm handy with the brand,
For I can ride a rowdy colt, or swing the axe all day,
But there's no demand for a station-hand along the Castlereagh.

Shift, boys, shift, there's not the slightest doubt
It's time to make a shift to the stations further out;
My pack-horse running after, he will follow like a dog.
We'll travel a lot of country at the old jig-jog.

As far as printed versions are concerned, 'The Stockman's Last Bed' is one of the most popular in Australia. The first known Australian source is *The Queenslanders' New Colonial Camp Fire Song Book* (1865), now correctly attributed to George Loyau, but it travelled far, as is shown by an undated (*c.* 1870) cutting from the *Cork Constitution* discovered by the late Dr E. Morris Miller. Several persons contributed versions of the song, some with very interesting background information, to the *Bulletin* between 1885 and 1888. Lee's version went like this:

THE STOCKMAN'S LAST BED

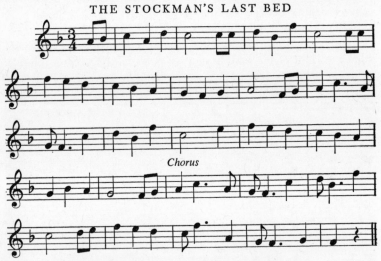

Chorus

Be you a stockman or not, to my story give ear;
Poor Jack, he is gone and no more we shall hear
The sound of his stockwhip, his steed's lively trot,
His clear 'Go ahead!', and his jingling quart-pot.

CHORUS:
 For he sleeps 'neath the wattle
 Their fragrance sweet sheds
 'Neath the tall gumtrees' shadows
 The stockman's last bed.

Colin Lee

One of the dance tunes played by Jack Lee's brother Colin was a varsovienne or, as he and most bushmen call it, varsovienna. John Meredith, as his collection grew, found that this dance was, and still is, immensely popular in outback districts. He has recorded over thirty tunes for the varsovienne. Sometimes a bush musician may have two distinct tunes for the dance, but most have a favourite.

The varsovienne, a variation on the Polish mazurka, originated about 1850 and soon became popular throughout Europe as a ballroom dance. When it migrated to Australia, strangely enough, the dance left the city and found a home in the outlying country districts.

A few of the tunes have a name, but generally the player will know his tune simply as 'The Varsovienna', or sometimes as 'Valse Vienna', implying that the dance has something in common with the Viennese waltz. Actually 'varsovienne' is the French name for the dance, deriving from Warsaw (Varsovie).

VARSOVIENNA

Mary and Tom Byrnes

John Meredith recorded Mary Byrnes singing in 1954. She was then aged about seventy-three years and living at the Sydney suburb of Concord. She was of Irish-Australian descent, and had spent her early life on a farm at Springside, a small village near Orange, New South Wales.

47

Her large repertoire was mostly of Irish derivation, for the Irish were numerous in the district. As was the case with most singers recorded by Meredith, Mary Byrnes knew two or three complete folk songs and a number of old popular songs and many fragments of all kinds. Most of her songs were learned from the itinerant Irish seasonal workers, harvesters and threshers who came to work at the farm. After tea was over the family usually gathered on the homestead veranda in the mild summer evenings to sing songs and be entertained by the casual hands.

THE WRECK OF THE *DANDENONG*

Oh, wild and furious blew the blast,
And the clouds were hanging round,
When the Dandenong *from Melbourne sailed,*
For Newcastle port was bound.
She had eighty-three poor souls on board;
Through the storm she cleaved her way,
And it's sad to relate of her terrible fate,
'Twas just off Jervis Bay.

While steering through the briny waves,
Her propelling shaft gave way,
And the waters they came pressing in,
Which filled them with dismay.
All hands on board did all they could
Till at length all hope was gone,
And they hoisted a signal of distress
On board of the Dandenong.

48

It was not long until a barque,
A brisk and lively crew,
Came bearing down, and the Captain cried,
'We'll see what we can do!'
Came bearing down with might and main
In spite of wind or wave.
They did all they could, as Christians would,
Those precious lives to save.

While some in boats they tried to reach,
That kind and friendly barque,
And numbers of their lives were saved,
And then night came on, pitch dark.
What mortal man then could do more,
When the storm increased on strong?
And the rest now sleep in the briny deep
Along with the Dandenong.

This was one of the songs learned by Mary Byrnes when she was a little girl. When asked about her age at the time, she laughed, held her hand, a couple of feet from the floor and said, 'When I was about that high!' We presume she meant eight or nine years of age.

The wreck described in the ballad occurred in September 1876. Meredith has recorded verses of this song from three other singers, one of whom learned it at Grenfell, and another at Captain's Flat, both places in New South Wales.

THE BLACK VELVET BAND

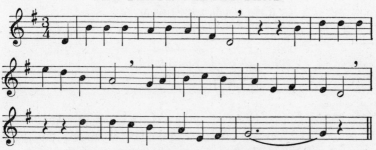

Oh, her eyes were like two shining diamonds,
And they called her the queen of our land,
And the hair that hung over her shoulders
Was tied with a black velvet band.

49

D

And before the judge I was taken,
And the jury said I was 'guiltee',
'You've been tried by your countrymen fairly,
You're a disgrace to your own native land.'

Other fragmentary versions of this song, as well as a complete variant, have been collected in Australia. It is known in Great Britain, and by a longer version ('The Blue Velvet Band') in North America, although there is no connection with the country-western song of the same name.

Another fragment contributed by Mary Byrnes was 'The Rich Old Farmer'.

THE RICH OLD FARMER

It's of a rich old farmer,
Who lived out there close by,
He had one only daughter,
And on her I cast an eye.

I asked her if she would be pleased
For me to cross the main,
Or if she would prove true to me
Till I returned again.

She said she would be true to me,
Till death would prove unkind,
And we kissed, shook hands and parted,
And I left my love behind. . . .

Here Mary Byrnes broke off with 'I don't know any more of it.'

A localized version of an Irish ballad of almost the same name is 'Whisky in the Jar'. A song of five stanzas with a different tune (except for the chorus) appears in Colm O Lochlainn's *Irish Street Ballads* under the title 'There's Whiskey in the Jar'. The Sir Frederick Pottinger of the local version was an inspector of police in the 1860s, and was scoffed at by the folk in the Weddin Mountains area (south-west of Orange) for his inability to catch the Ben Hall gang of bushrangers.

WHISKY IN THE JAR

As I was a-crossing the Abercrombie Mountain
I met Sir Frederick Pottinger and his money he was counting.
I first drew my blunderbuss and then I drew me sabre,
Saying, 'Stand and deliver all, for I'm your bold deceiver!'

CHORUS:
> *With me musha-ringa-dah*
> *Ri-tooral-addio*
> *There's whisky in the jar.*

I robbed him of his money; it was a pretty penny.
I robbed him of it all and I took it home to Molly.
I took it home to Molly and I thought she'd ne'er deceive me—
Ah, the devil's in the women for they never can be aisy.

I've got two brothers who are both in the army,
One is in Cork and another in Killarney.
If they were here tonight and all so free and jolly,
Tossing off another glass to my deceitful Molly.

Mrs Byrnes added, 'There is a little bit more that I've missed out on, but I forget the first part of it.'

The ballad called 'Donald of Glencoe' which Mrs Byrnes recorded carries the same theme as Mrs Popplewell's 'As I Was A-Walking'.

51

DONALD OF GLENCOE

As I went out walking, one evening of late,
Where's Flora's gay mantle was seen decorate,
I carelessly wandered, where I did not know,
To the banks of a fountain that lies in Glencoe.

When a lass did approach me as bright as the sun,
[Line missing]
With red crimson tassels, all round her did flow,
Where once lived young Donald, the pride of Glencoe.

I said, 'My dear lassie, your enchanting smile,
Uncommon sweet affection on you I'd beguile.
If your kind affection on me you'd bestow,
You'll bless the happy hours you roamed in Glencoe.'

She said, 'My dear laddie, your suit I'll disdain,
I once had a lover, young Donald by name;
He went to the war about seven years ago,
And a maid I'll remain till he returns to Glencoe.'

'Perhaps your young Donald did you disdain
And placed his affections on some foreign dame;
Or he might have forgotten, and you did not know,
The sweet lovely lassie he left in Glencoe.'

'My Donald's true promise shall never depart,
For there's love, truth and honour to be found in his heart.'
'Perhaps your young Donald, it may happen so,
Loved you most dearly, perhaps he's laid low.'

'My Donald's true virtue was tried on the field;
With his gallant ancestors, disdaining to yield,
The French and the Spaniards will soon overthrow,
And in splendour be returned to my arms in Glencoe.'

In finding her constant, I pulled out a glove
Which, in parting, she gave me as a token of love.
She hung on my breast while the tears overflowed—
She said, 'You're my Donald, returned to Glencoe!'

'*Cheer up, my dear Flora, your troubles are o'er;*
While life doth remain we will part nevermore.
The storms of the wars at a distance may blow,
Live in peace and content and reside in Glencoe.'

Will Ogilvie in his poem 'How the Fire Queen Crossed the Swamp' is one of the few versifiers who have commemorated the names of wagons. Yet Mary Byrnes had a fund of stories about wagons and the names bestowed upon them by their proud owners. (It is of interest to note that many present-day interstate truck drivers carry on this tradition by adding a name on the bonnet of their prime movers.)

'His name was old Paddy Ryan,' she said when telling John Meredith about the various wagons. 'He was the one who couldn't spell. A lot of the wagons had names printed on the sides of them, such as *Pull Me Through* and *I'm Coming* and *Here I Come* and *Mountain Maid* and *Morning Star*. And I remember an old chap named Paddy Ryan who used to go round from place to place and stay a few days, and he could neither read nor write; and he read out one morning, after getting up (he stayed at Mrs Hoey's place and he wanted to read out the name on the wagon), and he read out: "M-O-R-N-I-N-G, Dolphy; S-T-A-R, Hoey. Dolphy Hoey!"

'And my father called his wagon *Rock of Cashel*. He said that his horses could pull what all the horses in Ireland couldn't pull. Paddy Ryan was the chap who knew the Sandy Ross song (the one about the fight with Larry Foley). They were all horse wagons. They would only use bullock teams to draw off the logs after they fell the trees in bush paddocks; there were only a couple of bullock teams about there. They all had horse teams to carry the produce. They never carried produce with bullock teams. They were much slower.

'I can remember an old chap, a neighbour, a Mr Brennan; he had a bullock team. He used it to draw off the logs when they fell. It was new country and they cleared a lot of ground about there. They felled the trees, chopped them up in lengths and made log fences of them. Afterwards they burnt them because they were a harbour for the rabbits. Then they put up the wire fences, but in those days they would roll them to the side of the

53

paddock and put log upon log, and had the bullocks to draw them up. The bullocks were slow, but they gave a steady pull.

'You could always tell who owned the wagons by the names on them.'

Included in Mary Byrnes's group of songs were two very well-known ballads, both with close relations amongst the broadsides. The first, 'Castle Gardens', is also known as 'Convent Gardens' and 'Covent Gardens'.

CASTLE GARDENS

I bid farewell to relations and friends both one and all;
My lot is in America to rise or to fall,
For, alas, I am convicted and I am forced to go
And leave the shabbit island where the dear little shamrock grows.

CHORUS:
    Hurrah, my boys, the sails are set and the winds are blowing fair;
    We're bound for Castle Gardens, in a few days we'll be there.
    It's hard to part from those you love, and it's in my heart I know
    We're leaving dear old Ireland where the dear little shamrock
      grows.

Scotland may boast of the thistle and England of the rose,
But give to me old Ireland where the dear little shamrock grows.
And if you go the boys and girls will take you by the hand
And treat you all with whisky, too, in that dear old Paddy's land.

She waited for a little while, she fretted, and she died:
My only consolation—she sleeps by my father's side.
Both night and day went for to pray wherever we may roam,
And leave the shabbit island where the dear little shamrocks grow.

54

The tune of the second of the songs, 'Leaving Old England', has a marked similarity to that of 'Botany Bay', and perhaps may have been one model for the music-hall song. Mrs Byrnes sang several verses of 'Botany Bay' to almost the same tune as that given here.

LEAVING OLD ENGLAND

I've oft saw you smiling, dear mother,
Your dear face was beaming with joy.
Then why do you weep, dearest mother?
Be cheerful and answer your boy.

It's hard to be leaving old England,
But there's worse separations to see.
I'd rather be leaving, dear mother,
Could I carry thy blessing with me.

Then give me thy blessing, dear mother,
And weep not, oh, weep not for me;
There's a stormy cloud hangs o'er old England,
And a fortune across the deep sea.

Do you think I could see my dear sister,
Lying ill on a pallet of straw,
Not able to give her refreshment
Or keep her from Death's doving door?

Oh, no, I would rather be leaving
Old England's bright glittering shore,
And farewell to all friends that are grieving,
Farewell to old England e'er more.

There's a squire just a-going from his dwelling,
He's counting his wealth by the score;
If you take but one stick from his dwelling,
He'll put you to jail evermore.

You may boast of your Englishmen's freedom—
They're the first for to make you a slave;
They would take the bread from your children,
And transport you across the deep sea.

Then give me thy blessing, dear mother,
And weep not, oh, weep not for me;
There's a stormy cloud hangs o'er old England,
And a fortune across the deep sea.

When John Meredith returned to Mary Byrnes's home in 1955 he met her brother-in-law, Tom, aged sixty-six, who also came from the Springside-Springhill district. He sang a number of songs and lilted several quite good dance tunes. Tom Byrnes was at one time in great demand as a country fiddler, but owing to a hand injury he could no longer play.

The first song by Tom Byrnes was unusual in that, although nearly every bush musician plays this beautiful waltz tune, this was the only instance when words were given. A large number of variants exist for the tune.

A STARRY NIGHT FOR A RAMBLE

It's a starry night for a ramble
Through the flowery dell,
Over bush and bramble,
Kiss, but never tell.
Of all the games that I love best,
It fills me with delight;
I like to take a ramble
Upon a starry night.

Tom Byrnes had a version of Paterson's 'A Bushman's Song', which he called 'Travelling Down the Castlereagh'. He introduced it by saying, 'This is a song my father used to sing in my boy days' (that is, between 1900 and 1906).

TRAVELLING DOWN THE CASTLEREAGH

I'm travelling down the Castlereagh, and I'm a station-hand,
I'm handy with the roping pole, I'm handy with the brand,
I can ride a rowdy colt or two and swing the axe all day,
But there's no demand for a station-hand along the Castlereagh.

CHORUS:
 So it's shift, boys, shift, for there wasn't the slightest doubt
 We had to make a shift to the stations further out,
 With my pack-horse running after me, he follows like a dog,
 We left the scabby station with the old jig-jog.

Mary and Tom Byrnes each remembered a few verses of 'The Hut That's Upside Down', and after the third time through they agreed that the version given here was as close to the original as they could remember. The shed mentioned in the song was probably that on Big Burrawang, in the vicinity of Bogan Gate, central New South Wales, between Parkes and Condobolin. This shed was, in fact, so big that a wooden tramway ran around it to move the wool. Numerous tall stories are told of this place, all concerned with its remarkable size. Big Burrawang has now been subdivided for soldier settlement.

THE HUT THAT'S UPSIDE DOWN

Me name is Bobby Ambelet, to Glasgow I belong,
I've just stepped in among you all to sing to you a song.
I've travelled about the 'counteree' to places of renown,
But now I'm anchored hard and fast in the hut that's upside down.

CHORUS:
      The cook he danced the Highland fling, oh, Laddie plays the lute,
      The little boy from Burraway he played upon the flute,
      Scotty he sings 'The Mulberry Tree', and all dull care is flown.
      We're happy as larks out in the park in the hut that's upside down.

The shearing it has now begun, the machines are doing well,
The little shears they go 'click-click', and the wool rolls off pell-mell.
The tramway runs around the board, the boys are flying around,
And the cook is lashing the brownie out in the hut that's upside down.

The other night I went to read and went to sleep quite sound;
I thought the hut was all agee [agley] and I was on the ground.
When I awoke, to my surprise the boys were standing round,
And the cook was lashing the brownie out in the hut that's upside down.

At night we pass the hours away at euchre, nap and bluff,
Others rhyme to kill their time, while others blow their stuff.
There was prime roast beef for dinner and the duff was served
    around;
We're getting as fat as poisoned pups in the hut that's upside down.

Well, it's now, me boys, I must away; I hope no one will frown,
But give three cheers for Willie the cook in the hut that's upside down.

On the day that Tom and Mary were recalling the verses of
this song, two friends—Alf Fuller and Harry Ascough—called on
a visit and were persuaded by John to record.

Alf Fuller, of Concord, sang 'Five Bob to Four' and 'Aboard
of the *Kangaroo*'. 'Five Bob to Four' he learned from his father,
who in turn had it from some travelling threshers at Lewis
Ponds. Now an extinct race, gangs of reapers, threshers, and
chaff-cutters were responsible for spreading many of our folk
songs.

FIVE BOB TO FOUR

It was over at MacRose's where the threshing first began—
He is a little podgy, a jolly little man,
And every time the whistle blew, at the closing of the day,
He was no ways backward in coming with the pay.
Four bob a day, is all that he could pay—

I hope his cows the measles take, his hens refuse to lay,
For cutting down the wages to four bob a day.
I hope his pumpkins all take rot, his haystacks and his straw,
For cutting down the wages from five bob to four.

Fuller also learned 'Aboard of the *Kangaroo*' from his father. Burl Ives has recorded another version on a disc devoted to Irish folk songs.

ABOARD OF THE *KANGAROO*

Cheer up, cheer up, my own true love,
Don't weep so bitterly.
She sobbed, she sighed, she choked and cried,
And could not say goodbye.
I shan't be gone so very long—
Just only a month or two—
But when I do return again
Of course I will marry you.
[4 lines missing]
I never thought that she'd prove false,
Or ever be untrue,
As I sailed away from Ilford Bay
On board of the Kangaroo.

'Jacky Me Lad' was learned by Harry Ascough from his father. It is a rhyme chanted rather than sung, and, apart from a certain underlying bawdiness, it might be a traditional nursery rhyme.

JACKY ME LAD

Oh, Jacky me lad, he loved his dad,
He put him in a peer flad [sic];
The peer flad it was so thick
They put him in the bacon click;
The bacon click it was so fat,
They put him in old grand-dad's hat;
Old grand-dad's hat it was so big,
They put him in his hairy wig;
His hairy wig it was so hairy,
They put him into bed with Mary;
Mary kicked and bucked about,
Until she kicked, and knocked him out.

Edwin Goodwin

John Meredith was introduced to Edwin Goodwin by Dr Ces English, who had attended the old man at the Royal Prince Alfred Hospital, had several conversations with him on the subject of folk songs and learned 'Dennis O'Reilly' from him. When Goodwin, who was then aged seventy-three years, had recovered from his illness he called on Meredith at Lewisham. An afternoon was spent recording songs and talking about old times.

Ted Goodwin had for most of his working life been a timber-cutter in the Nambucca River district on the North Coast of New South Wales, and there he learned his songs. He sang them very slowly, with the exception of a couple of 'comics', and in a fine clear deep voice. This singer had a curious and inimitable mannerism of sliding down an interval of two tones at the end of some lines, which gave an interesting quality to his singing.

Like that of Mary Byrnes, the larger part of his repertoire had a distinct Irish flavour, including such ballads as 'Biddy from Donegal' and 'Mary, Lovely Mary'.

Edwin Goodwin died in 1955, a few months after John Meredith had recorded his songs.

Other versions of 'Dennis O'Reilly', fragments only, were recorded by Jamie Carlin and Cyril Ticehurst of Kogarah (Ticehurst called his song 'Tramp the Bushes of Australia'). It seems likely that the various versions fathered the one printed by Paterson as 'With My Swag All On My Shoulder' in *Old Bush Songs*. The tune derives from an American railroad song, 'Casey, Go and Oil That Car'.

My name is Dennis O'Reilly,
From Dublin town I came;
For to sail the world all over,
I sailed for the Australian main.
With my pack upon my shoulder
And a blackthorn in my hand,
I'll travel the bushes of Australia
Like a true-born Irishman.

When I arrived in Melbourne town,
The girls all jumped with joy,
Said one unto the other,
'Here comes my Irish boy.
With his pack upon his shoulder
And a blackthorn in his hand,
For to travel the bushes of Australia
Like a true-born Irishman.'

'Oh, daughter, dearest daughter,
What do you intend to do,
For to fall in love with an Irishman
A man you never knew?'
[4 lines forgotten]

'Oh, mother, dearest mother,
I'll do the best I can;
I'll travel the bushes of Australia
With my true-born Irishman.
With my pack upon my shoulder
And a blackthorn in my hand,
I'll travel the bushes of Australia
With my true-born Irishman.'

Goodwin made use of the 'Irish Molly-Oh' tune for his version of 'The Wild Colonial Boy' and 'Bold Jack Donahoe'. Probably the tune is best known for its use in 'Jim Jones at Botany Bay'.

BOLD JACK DONAHOE

If you'll but listen, a sorrowful tale I'll tell,
Concerning a young hero, in action lately fell.
His name it was Jack Donahoe, of courage and renown;
He'd scorn to live in slavery or be humbled to the Crown.

On the twenty-fourth of August, it be his fatal day,
As he and his companions were cruising the highway,
He was hailed by the horse police, he stood with heart and hand;
'Come on, my lads!' cried Donahoe. 'We'll fight them man for man.'

Says he to his companions, 'Now, if you're only game—
You'll see there's only three of them, our number's just the same.
[Line forgotten]
For today it's life or liberty, or fall upon the plain.'

'Oh, no,' says cowardly Walmsley, 'your laws we'll not fulfil;
You'll see there's eight or ten of them advancing on yon hill.
If it comes to an engagement, you'll rue it when too late,
So turn about and come with me, we'll form a quick retreat.'

'Begone you cowardly scoundrels! Begone, I pray, from me.
For if we were united we'd gain this victory.
Today I'll fight with courage bold that all the world may see;
For I'd rather die in battle than be hung on a gallows tree.'

Soon they commenced their firing. Poor Donahoe did say,
'My curse lay on you, Walmsley, for from me you've run away!'
The one played off in front of him, the others at each side;
At length he received a mortal wound and in his glory died.

The equals of Jack Donahoe this country has never seen,
He did maintain his rights, my boys, and that right manfully.
He was chased about by hundreds for three long years or more,
Until at length the heavens decreed that he should roam no more.

The awful end of Donahoe, the truth to you I've told,
And hope that all good Christians will pray for his soul.
May the Holy Angels guard him, likewise our Heavenly King,
And our Saviour dear who died for us redeem his soul from sin.

'Bound for Charlers Town', under a variety of names, is
known to many singers recorded by John Meredith, and has an
analogue in the street ballad 'Bound for Sydney Town', as sung
by Gladys Scrivener. Almost similar texts exist in print as English broadsides dating back to 1830. Ticehurst's 'Moreton's Bay'
appears to be a variant of either Goodwin's or Scrivener's song.

The word 'trinkling' was at first considered to be a corruption of 'twinkling' or 'trickling', but then Mary Byrnes, Sally
Sloane, and later Tom Gibbons at Gulgong used it also. An early
use of this archaic word was in Captain Cook's *Journal* when
he described the water running in a stream at Botany Bay.

Sometimes the ballad is called 'The Boston Burglar'. 'Charlers
Town' is the usual corruption of Charleston, South Carolina,
once a port of entry for British convicts shipped to America.
The ballad-singer's pronunciation has been retained here.

BOUND FOR CHARLERS TOWN

I was born in Boston City, boys, a place you all know well,
Brought up by honest parents and the truth to you I'll tell;
Brought up by honest parents and reared most tenderly,
Till I became a roving lad at the age of twenty-three.

My character was broken and I was sent to jail;
My parents tried to bail me out but it was of no avail.
The jury found me guilty and the clerk he wrote it down,
Saying, 'Oh, my boy, for seven long years, you're bound for Charlers
　　Town.'

They put me on an east-bound train, on a cold and stormy day,
And every station we passed by, you would hear the people say,
'There goes a known vagrant, in iron chains he's bound;
For the robbery of the Boston bank, he's bound for Charlers Town.'

It grieved my aged father, while standing at the bar,
Likewise my poor old mother, a-tearing of her hair;
A-tearing of her old grey locks whilst the tears came trinkling down,
Saying, 'Oh, my son, what have you done! You're bound for Charlers
　　Town.'

There's a girl in Boston city, boys, a girl you all know well,
And if ever I gain my freedom, it's along with her I'll dwell;
I'll give up all night walking, bad company I'll shun.
Take my advice to any young man: leave off drinking of the rum.

All those who have got their liberty, keep it while they can,
Or else like me they'll surely rue the serving of the penalty.
It grieved my aged father, whilst pleading at the bar,
Likewise my tender mother, a-tearing of her hair;
A-tearing of her old grey locks, whilst the tears came trinkling down,
Saying, 'Oh, my son, what have you done! You're bound for Charlers
　　Town.'

ARTHUR NOLAN

E

Kind friends, give your attention and a story I will tell
About poor Arthur Nolan, the jockey you all know well.
Whilst riding a horse called Sulphide in the Sydney Steeplechase
His mount came down, fell over him, smashed in his head and face.

Poor lad, his mother was not there to bid her boy goodbye;
Poor Archie Nolan stood like stone with a teardrop in his eye.
'I'm sorry I ever let him ride,' good Mr Burgo said,
But alas, kind friends, it was too late, for the jockey lay there dead.

Then draw in lines, down goes the flag, the horses tear away,
You'd have thought it was a flat race by the pace they went that day.
Poor Arthur urged his mount along in trying to catch Wild Dog,
When Arthur's mount fell over him just like a floating log.

Then Archie he remounted and he quietly walked away,
And the horses thundered o'er the jumps on that scorching summer's
*   day.*
See Sulphide thunder at the jumps, as around the back they turn;
When he came down, smash, on his plucky jock, poor Arthur lay there
*   dead.*

Poor lad, his mother was not there to bid her boy goodbye;
Poor Archie Nolan stood like stone with a teardrop in his eye.
'I'm sorry I ever let him ride,' good Mr Burgo said,
But alas, kind friends, it was too late, for the jockey lay there dead.

Now all you jockeys take warning when you ride in a steeplechase,
On a horse that is not fit and well, don't try to make the pace;
Or you'll find like poor young Nolan you'll never reach the goal,
And in conclusion I must say, Lord have mercy on his soul.

Poor lad, his mother was not there to bid her boy good bye;
Poor Archie Nolan stood like stone with a teardrop in his eye.
'I'm sorry I ever let him ride,' good Mr Burgo said,
But alas, kind friends, it was too late, for the jockey lay there dead.

In a country where horse racing is so popular, it is strange
that the ballads dealing with the deaths of several famous
jockeys, and the wins of a number of champion horses, should
have been ignored by collectors of native songs.

Arthur Nolan, the subject of the racing 'Come-all-ye' above,
was said by Goodwin to be a jockey in the Newcastle district.

Edwin Goodwin included a brief version of an immigrant's
song. A longer text was supplied by Jack Wright (see p. 131).

Oh, I'm sixteen thousand miles from home;
My heart is sorely aching
To think that I should humble down
To come out here stone-breaking.
The road I took to Castlemaine,
And I met a sub-contractor,
He looked at me and thus did say,
'Are you a parson or a doctor?'
With me osey-oorey-oorey-ay,
Ri-tiddy-fol-lol-lo-ly-o.

Your hands are white, your face is pale,
Your toggery's of the finest,
You look to me as an immigrant
Who's been using water and shining
With me osey-oorey-oorey-ay,
Ri-tiddy-fol-lol-lo-ly-o.

Sally Sloane and John Linigen, as well as Goodwin, sang versions of 'The Convict's Return', a long sentimental popular song written by Leonard Nelson and sung by him throughout the eastern States during the 1890s. Goodwin's version has been chosen for reproduction here.

It's just ten years ago tonight, they dragged me from my wife,
They charged me with that awful crime, the taking of a life.
The judge, the courthouse sentence, the judge says, 'You must die.'
But bear up, my dear heart we'll meet in heaven most high.

CHORUS:

But where is the wife I left behind, my pride, my love and joy?
Why did she roam from her dear old home? Where is my baby boy?
Gone is the manly strength I had, my temple would throb and burn—

There's no one to meet, there's no one to greet: it's only a convicts return.
There's no one to meet, there's no one to greet: it's only a convicts return.

Days, weeks, months, and years rolled on, it seemed to me a dream;
Escape, escape, my only chance, how impossible it seemed.
It was on a dark December night, beneath the walls I heard
The sentry pass, and, safe at last, one mighty leap I made.

I'm on the wall—I'm over. Hurrah! Hurrah! I'm free!
But what is that dark object there—can it a sentry be?
'Halt! halt!' he cries, 'or else I'll fire,' came ringing through the night.
I turned and fled, I knew no more, he shot me in my flight.

One day the chaplain of the jail came unto me and said,
'Cheer up, cheer up, my good man. Praise heavens, you are free!
The day you quarrelled with your friend, you did not kill him, no,
Another came and saw him stunned and struck him that foul blow.
You'll leave this place tomorrow, your name and your conscience clear,
And safe back to your dear old home, to those you love so dear.'

Possibly the best of the several versions of 'Wild Rover' given
in this book was sung by Goodwin. Its distinction comes from
an unusual tune in the Aeolian mode.

WILD ROVER

I've been a wild rover for many long years,
And I've spent all my money in whisky and beer,
But the time now is approaching, I must take care,
For fear that misfortune should fall to my share.

Wild roving, bold roving,
Wild roving give o'er,
For I ne'er shall be
A wild rover no more.

Arthur Buchanan

Arthur Buchanan was born in 1892 and died in 1957. He was an Anzac and lost both legs in World War I. It was on Gallipoli that he learned 'Sing Me to Sleep' and 'The Barley-mow', the latter always very popular with the other Diggers in the hospital.

THE BARLEY-MOW

Here's good luck to the gill-pot, good luck to the barley-mow,
Here's good luck to the gill-pot, good luck to the barley-mow.
For gill-pot, have a gill, have a good gill in the Elegy Bar,
Here's good luck, good luck to the barley-mow.

Here's good luck to the pint-pot, good luck to the barley-mow,
Oh, here's good luck to the pint-pot, good luck to the barley-mow.
Oh pint-pot, gill-pot, have a gill, have a good gill in the Elegy Bar,
Here's good luck, good luck to the barley-mow.

Here's good luck to the quart-pot, good luck to the barley-mow,
Here's good luck to the quart-pot, good luck to the barley-mow.
Oh quart-pot, pint-pot, gill-pot, have a gill, have a good gill in the
    Elegy Bar,
Here's good luck, good luck to the barley-mow.

Here's good luck to the half-gallon, good luck to the barley-mow,
Here's good luck to the half-gallon, good luck to the barley-mow.
Oh half-gallon, quart-pot, pint-pot, gill-pot, have a gill, have a good
    gill in the Elegy Bar,
Here's good luck, good luck to the barley-mow.

Here's good luck to the gallon, good luck to the barley-mow,
Here's good luck to the gallon, good luck to the barley-mow.
The gallon, half-gallon and quart-pot, pint-pot, gill-pot, have a gill,
    have a good gill in the Elegy Bar,
Here's good luck, good luck to the barley-mow.

Here's good luck to the half-barrel, etc.
Here's good luck to the barrel, etc.
Here's good luck to the barmaid, etc.
Here's good luck to the barman, etc.

A different tune to a longer version appeared in *A Dorset Book of Folk Songs* by Brocklebank and Kindersley. This was collected from a J. Caddy of Melplash who wished good luck to the nipperkin, quarter-pint nipperkin, half-pint, pint, quart, gallon, flagon, firkin, barrel, hogshead, butt, and tun! There was also a spoken line—'Can you drink out of the half-pint?'—before each verse, apparently to give a lead in community singing.

A large number of variants exist. William Chappell printed a traditional version in *Popular Music of the Olden Time* (p. 745) and his earlier *National English Airs* (1838). Cecil Sharp gives versions of this 'harvest health' in both *Folk Songs from Somerset*, Fifth Series (1909), and *English Folk Songs*, selected edition (1921). Most texts are accompanied by notes on the ceremony of cutting the last sheaf and 'crying the neck', an ancient pagan rite. 'A good singer,' wrote Sharp in his notes in *Folk Songs from Somerset*, 'proud of his memory, will often lengthen the song to abnormal proportions by halving the drink measures, half-pint, half-quart, half-gallon, and so on.'

Of his other songs, Arthur Buchanan learned 'The Wild

Colonial Boy' and 'Waltzing Matilda' from his father, who lived in the New England district of Armidale. Buchanan senior was a shearer for many years.

THE WILD COLONIAL BOY

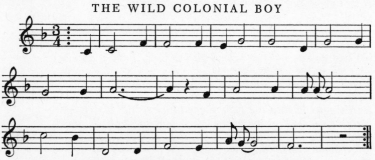

'Twas of a wild colonial boy, Jack Doolan was his name,
He was his mother's pride and joy that lived in Castlemaine.
He was but sixteen years of age when he left his father's home
Across Australia's sunny clime a bushranger to roam.

He robbed those lonely squatters, their sheep he did destroy,
A terror to the Victorians was that wild colonial boy.
And he stuck up the mailcoach and robbed Judge MacEvoy,
Who trembling gave up his gold to the wild colonial boy.

One day whilst on the mountain as he gaily rode away
Approached three mounted troopers—Kelly, Davies, and Fitzroy.
'Surrender now!' said Kelly, 'You see we're three to one;
Surrender in the Queen's name, you daring highwayman!'

Jack drew a pistol from his belt and waved the little toy.
'I'll fight but not surrender!' said the wild colonial boy.
He fired on Sergeant Kelly and brought him to the ground,
But in return from Davies received a mortal wound.

He grinned and bore it as he fell, still firing on Fitzroy,
For that is how they captured the wild colonial boy.
He bade the judge good morning and told him to beware
And never try to hang a man who acted on the square.

Arthur Buchanan told John Meredith that his father never went shearing after he married in 1885, yet 'Waltzing Matilda' was one of the songs learned while shearing. According to the 'Banjo' Paterson—Christina Macpherson legend, Paterson wrote 'Waltzing Matilda' in 1894. Another informant, Fred Sloane of Teralba, New South Wales, stated that his father learned the song in 1876, in the Monaro district near the Snowy River, from an old man called 'Old Blucher'.

May and other writers have asserted that the tune is derived from an arrangement of 'Thou Bonny Woods of Craigielea', but most people realize that 'Waltzing Matilda' is simply a parody on 'The Bold Fusilier', which was widely sung in this country during the nineteenth century. Other evidence exists to support the view that Paterson did not actually compose the ballad, but polished up an existing song, one which already had established itself in oral circulation.

'Craigielea' lacks even a superficial resemblance to 'Waltzing Matilda' as we know it today; one has, however, only to look at the text of 'The Bold Fusilier' to see the similarity:

A bold fusilier was marching down through Rochester,
Bound for the wars in the Low Country,
And he cried as he tramped through the dear streets of Rochester,
'Who'll be a sojer for Marlbro' with me?

'Who'll be a sojer, who'll be a sojer,
Who'll be a sojer for Marlbro' with me?'
And he cried as he tramped through the dear streets of Rochester,
'Who'll be a sojer for Marlbro' with me?'

WALTZING MATILDA

A swagman sat, on the banks of the billybong.
Under the shade of a coolabah tree,
And he sat and sang and waited till his billy boiled,
'You'll come a-waltzing matilda with me.'

> *'Waltzing matilda, waltzing matilda,*
> *You'll come a-waltzing matilda with me.'*
> *For he sat and sang and waited till his billy boiled,*
> *'You'll come a-waltzing matilda with me.'*

Up jumped a jumbuck and hopped into the willybung,
Up jumped the swagman, one, two, three!
Oh, he killed that jumbuck and put him in his tuckerbag;
'You'll come a-waltzing matilda with me.'

> *'Waltzing matilda, waltzing matilda,*
> *You'll come a-waltzing matilda with me.'*
> *For he sat and sang and waited till his billy boiled,*
> *'You'll come a-waltzing matilda with me.'*

Up came the troopers mounted on their thoroughbreds,
Up came the troopers, one, two, three!
'Where's that jumbuck you've got there in your tuckerbag?
You'll come a-waltzing matilda with me.'

> *'Waltzing matilda, waltzing matilda,*
> *You'll come a-waltzing matilda with me,'*
> *'Where's that jumbuck you've got there in your tuckerbag?*
> *You'll come a-waltzing matilda with me.'*

Up jumped the swagman and jumped into the billabong,
'You'll never take me alive,' said he.
And his ghost may be heard as you walk along that billabong,
'You'll come a-waltzing matilda with me.'

> *'Waltzing matilda, waltzing matilda,*
> *You'll come a-waltzing matilda with me.'*
> *And his ghost may be heard as you walk along that billabong,*
> *'You'll come a-waltzing matilda with me.'*

The song of 'Young Les Darcy', as sung by Arthur Buchanan, was obviously the work of a sophisticated musician, but, along with the other Darcy song, the parody on 'Way Down in Tennessee', it passed into the oral tradition. 'Young Les Darcy' is in the style of the popular songs of the second decade of this century, such as 'There's a Long, Long Trail a-Winding' and 'The

Rose of No Man's Land'. No doubt, too, a simpler person would have used a tune with a four-line, sixteen-bar arrangement.

Both Darcy songs are still popular among the older singers.

YOUNG LES DARCY

We all get a craving to roam
Far from home, o'er the foam;
We long other lands for to see,
And the thought fills our hearts with glee.
An Australian lad we know so well,
Who journeyed to add to his fame—
You all know the story,
It's covered with glory,
A fairer one ne'er played the game.

CHORUS:

> *That was young Les Darcy,*
> *Who we know was so ill advised,*
> *And when the sad news reached us,*
> *How the tears bedimmed our eyes.*
> *He had one great ambition—*
> *'Twas to fight at the Golden Gate.*
> *But the voice that called him from us*
> *Proved to be the sad bells of fate.*

Picture his loved ones at home,
How they mourn, now he's gone.
So modest and thoughtful was he,
A fairer one ne'er could be.
The world is the poorer today
By the loss of that champion so fine,
We will all regret him,
But none will forget him;
His memory with laurel we'll twine.

The origin of 'Young Les Darcy' is uncertain, but the song is markedly similar in text and tune to a coalfields song from the Maitland district, 'A Sad Day on the Coalfields', which was written by R. Grant on the death of Norman Brown.

Darcy was born at Woodville, near Maitland, New South Wales, in 1895, and died in Memphis, U.S.A., on 24th May 1917. He went to America at a time when anti-conscription battles were being fought through Australia. Les had attempted to enlist, but, as a minor, was unable to get his parents' consent. He was feasted and fêted on his arrival in the States, but suddenly the publicity was turned against him. The Governor of New York refused Darcy permission to box and branded him as a slacker. Finally, a match was arranged between Darcy and Len Rowlands in Memphis, Tennessee. It was while training for this bout that he became ill and died—of a broken heart, according to some old singers.

Joe Cashmere

Joe Cashmere was a man with a buoyant sense of humour. Recording sessions with him always assumed the character of a light-hearted musical afternoon: Meredith would take out his button accordion, sometimes Jeffrey Way went along with his guitar, and, of course, Joe would bring out his old fiddle which had been in use for over sixty years.

Cashmere once wrote for the *Albury Banner*, the *Bulletin*, and the *Worker*, but it was as a performer of song snatches, recitations and yarns that he shone. He was in his mid-eighties when Meredith was visiting him; nevertheless, he was still a man of spirit and vitality.

He told his visitors about a dance called 'The Bullocky's Schottische' which was regarded as extremely vulgar, and claimed he had seen policemen prevent its being danced in the bush. He demonstrated the steps. It turned out to be much the same as the usual schottische, with the addition of a suggestive thrust of the hips at the end of every third step!

One of Joe Cashmere's tricks was to make his old fiddle sound like the bagpipes. He would slip his tobacco-pipe under the strings, just behind the bridge, where it curiously distorted the tone. The D string was played as a drone and the melody beaten out on the A string.

The fiddle sounded a bit scratchy after being humped about the bush for so many years, but the old fellow always managed perfect dance time, and with many a little decoration and turn in the melody. He did not read music, but learned his tunes by listening attentively at bush dances or whenever he had an opportunity of hearing an outback town band. Once he shore in a shed with the son of a band conductor and learned a few tunes from him during the run. Cashmere told Meredith that often he would hear a tune at a dance and then be unable to recall it until three or four days had passed, when it would suddenly come to mind. His practice was then to whistle and sing it over and over until he had committed it to memory.

77

A nineteenth-century ballroom dance which spread through Europe from its native Poland, the polka-mazurka—and the so-called varsovienna—persisted in the country areas of Australia long after going out of fashion in the cities. When John Meredith had recorded Joe Cashmere's tunes for the polka-mazurka and the varsovienna, Joe and his wife danced the steps.

POLKA-MAZURKA

Joe had a great deal to say about the varsovienna in bygone times.

'We held a dance in a back-station woolshed,' he said reminiscently, 'and there was a young policeman there, a young policeman from Booligal—he came out to the dance and we had a bottle of whisky down every chute in the shed, and we all got pretty well full of hops.

'Anyway,' he continued after a pause, 'I played [the varsovienna]. And they had never heard it before, and, oh, they reckoned it was lovely! Anyway, time went on and he [the policeman] left Booligal. I got away, and I think it was thirty years after—I was down here, and I put up at Molong one evening—I stopped at Molong. Just about sundown a sergeant came along with a big sort of ginger moustache. He came up to me, and looked at me a while, and said, "I think I've seen you before."

' "I dunno," I says. "You might have seen me at Long Bay."

' "No, it wasn't at Long Bay. No, I've seen you somewhere before."

' "Well," I said, "I can't say that I've seen you," I said. "If I did it must have been a long while ago."

'He said, "Was you ever at Booligal?"

' "Oh, too right," I said. "That was where I kicked off; that was my startin' point."

'He said, "Was ever you at a dance?" he said, "at a back-station woolshed, playin' that violin?"

'I said, "I was."

'He said, "I'll never forget that varsovienna," he said. "Don't you remember me?"

'I said, "No."

'He said, "I was that policeman there that was boozing up with you."

'It was years after, but he still remembered me, you see—it was that varsovienna.'

Still smiling at the thought, Joe took up his scratchy fiddle and played. As he said, it was a sweet lilting tune, and he played it lightly and in perfect dance time.

VARSOVIENNA

continued

Mick Pilley of Mudgee and Sally Sloane both play a varso-vienna the first part of which is different from Cashmere's first section while the second tune is the same as Cashmere's second.

A waltz played by Mick Pilley, 'I've Got a Saviour That's Mighty to Keep', is a simple binary tune. The variant, 'Orphan Boy Waltz', played by Joe Cashmere has no less than five parts, which is most unusual among bush musicians. It is possible, of course, that Cashmere may have unconsciously combined two or three tunes into one whole, but, if he did so, they are remarkably similar. This tune, in another variant form, is used for the well-known student comic song, 'Just for the Ride':

> *He sat by the window and smoked his cigar,*
> *Smoked his cigar, smoked his cigar,*
> *He sat by the window and smoked his cigar,*
> *Smoked his cigar-ha-ha-ha!*

ORPHAN BOY WALTZ

The Sydney Flash is a name given to a special stockwhip crack, a triple crack; it has been transferred to a step-dance, or

F

solo jig, which was popular last century with the larrikin push of the Sydney Rocks area at Miller's Point—where, incidentally, there is still to be found a 'cellar-flap' dancer. This kind of dance consists of a jig on a cellar cover, with the flap creating a resonance and amplification of the tapping feet.

It will be noticed that the tune finishes with three staccato notes; possibly the dancer ended with three stamps of the feet.

THE SYDNEY FLASH

Cashmere said that sometimes two men would have a challenge dance to see who knew the greatest number of steps, or who would tire first. Occasionally, a dancer tried to outdance the musician.

One of the solo jig tunes used is particularly attractive:

STEP-DANCE (JIG)

Although Joe Cashmere and his mate Jack Lee learned 'The Old Jig-jog' at Booligal about the same time, they sang, as has been mentioned earlier, variant tunes. (Lee's appears on p. 45).

THE OLD JIG-JOG

I'm travelling down the Castlereagh, I am a station hand,
I'm handy with the roping pole, I'm handy with the brand,
And I can ride a rowdy colt, or swing an axe all day,
But there's no demand for a station-hand along the Castlereagh.

> *Shift, boys, shift, there's not the slightest doubt*
> *It's time to make a shift to the stations farther out,*
> *Your pack-horse running after, he follows you like a dog,*
> *We travel a lot of country at the old jig-jog.*

This old black horse I'm riding—if you wish to know his brand,
He's branded with the crooked R—none better in the land.
He takes a lot of beating; the other day we tried,
For a bit of a joke, with a racy bloke, for twenty pound a side.

It was shift, boys, shift, there wasn't the slightest doubt
We had to make him shift for our money was near run out,
But he cantered home a winner, while the other one had to flog—
He's a good old sort for the pick up, with his old jig-jog.

I asked a bloke for shearing once, down on the Marthaguy:
'We shear non-union here,' he said. 'I call it scab,' said I.
I looked along the shearing board before I chanced to go—
Saw eight to ten dashed Chinamen all shearing in a row.

It was shift, boys, shift, there's not the slightest doubt
For it's time I made a shift with the leprosy about.
I saddled up my horses, and I whistled to my dog;
I left that scabby station at the old jig-jog.

I called at Illawarra, where my brother keeps a farm;
He has to ask the landlord's leave before he'd raise an arm:
The landlord owns the countryside—man, woman, dog, and cat,
They haven't the cheek to dare to speak unless they raise their hat.

It was shift, boys, shift, there's not the slightest doubt
That squatter chap and I we would soon be falling out;
Was I to raise my hat to him?—was I a blooming dog?
I struck for up the country at the old jig-jog.

'That's an old convict one—that's all I know of that 'n',' said
Joe as he finished singing the chorus of 'Ten Thousand Miles
Away'. A pity, since it is the only localized version so far en-
countered.

TEN THOUSAND MILES AWAY

Blow you winds hey-ho,
A-roving I will go,
I'll stay no more on England's shore
To hear your music play.

I'm off by the morning train
To cross the One-tree Plain;
I'm taking a trip in a government ship
Ten thousand miles away.

Russel Ward collected the second and third verses of 'Caledonia' from Cashmere; these were afterwards recorded by Jeffrey Way and Edgar Waters. Twelve months later, when asked to sing the two verses at a meeting of the Australian Folk Lore Society, Cashmere astonished the members by recollecting seven. He told John Meredith that in Booligal in the late 1890s he saw police stop men singing this and other convict and bushranger ballads as treasonable. Jack Lee corroborated his statement.

CALEDONIA

My name is Jimmy Randall, in Glasgow I was born;
All through a sad misfortune, I was forced to leave in scorn.
From my home and occupation I was forced to gang awa',
And leave those bonnie hills of dear old Caledonia.

It was early one morning, before the break of day,
There came a cruel turnkey who unto us did say:
'Rise up, you seven convicts. I warn you, one and a',
It is today you sail away from Caledonia.'

We slowly rose, put on our clothes, our hearts were sad with grief;
Our friends, they came to see us off, could give us no relief.
With heavy chains they bound us down, for fear we'd gang awa'
Far from those bonnie hills and dales of Caledonia.

Goodbye unto my father, he was the best of men;
Likewise unto my sister, her name is Catheren.
Her bonny locks of auburn hair, I loved them that she wore;
She far excels those haughty belles of Caledonia.

85

Farewell unto my mother, I was her darling son;
I hope they won't cast up to her the reckless life I've run.
Heaven guard her and protect her now I am far awa',
Far from the place where I was born in Caledonia.

My sweetheart came to see me and bid a long goodbye;
She said to me, 'Goodbye, my man!' as in the cell I lie.
No more we'll roam together, down by old Broomielaw,
For the rolling seas divide us now from Caledonia.

I'm longing for the time to come when I'll again be free;
I'll lose no time in going home across the deep blue sea,
And see once more the ones I loved, as in the days of yore,
And find the sweetheart whom I left in Caledonia.

Another song of Cashmere's collected by Russel Ward, and taped by Way and Waters and subsequently printed in *Speewa* (the journal of the Australian Folk Lore Society), was 'Jog Along Till Shearing'. The old man said the tune was known as 'Miss Tickle Toby's School', but he also played on his fiddle the original music-hall tune—'Bow, Wow, Wow'—from which this was derived.

JOG ALONG TILL SHEARING

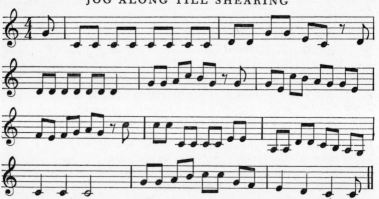

The truth it's in my song so clear, without a word of gammon:
The swagmen travel all the year, waiting for the lambin';
Now when this dirty work is done, to the nearest shanty steerin',
They meet a friend, their money spend, then jog along till shearin'.

CHORUS:
> *Singing home, sweet home,*
> *That is what they left it for,*
> *Their home, sweet home.*

Now when the shearing season comes, they hear the price that's going;
New arrivals meet old chums, then they start their blowing.
They say that they can shear each day their hundred pretty handy,
But eighty sheep is no child's play if the wool is close and sandy.

When the sheds are all cut out they get their bit of paper;
To the nearest pub they run—they cut a dashing caper.
They call for liquor plenty, and they're happy while they're drinking,
But where to go when the money's done, it's little they are thinking.

Sick and sore next morning, they are when they awaken;
To have a drink, of course they must to keep their nerves from shakin'.
They call for one, and then for two, in a way that's rather funny,
Till the landlord says, 'Now this won't do—you men have got no
    money.'

They're sleeping on verandas and they're lounging on the sofas;
For to finish up their spree, they're ordered off as loafers.
They've got no friends, their money's gone, and at their disappearing
They give three cheers for the river bends and jog along till shearing.

It is not often that a bush musician can sing to his playing, or
a folk-singer play his own accompaniment, but Joe Cashmere
became one of the exceptions as he fiddled his accompaniment to
'Wild Rover No More'. Other versions of the same song were
sung by Edwin Goodwin and Collie Bourke.

WILD ROVER NO MORE

87

I've been a wild rover for many a year,
I've spent all my money in whisky and beer,
And now I've returned with a flamin' great score;
Never be called a wild rover no more.

CHORUS:
    No, no, never, never no more,
    Never, never again will I be
    A wild rover no more.

I went to a shanty I used to frequent,
And I told the landlady my money was spent.
I asked her for credit, she answered me 'Nay',
Saying, 'Customers like you I can get any day.'

Then I drew from my pocket ten sovereigns bright,
And the landlady's eyes opened wide with delight.
Said she, 'I have whisky and wines of the best,
And the words that I uttered were only in jest.'

I'll go home to my parents, tell them what I have done,
And ask them to pardon their prodigal son,
And if they will do so as often before,
I never shall play the wild rover no more.

Madge Laver and Violet Skuthorpe

During the summer of 1958 Russel Ward sent Meredith the text
of a song called 'Paddy Sheahan', which he had obtained from
Madge Laver, a daughter of Lance Skuthorpe. She recorded it,
as well as a lovely version of 'The Dying Stockman', for John
Meredith at a later date.

PADDY SHEAHAN

My name is Paddy Sheahan, my age is twenty-four,
Tipperary is my native place, not far from Galtymore.
I came of honest parents, but now they are lying low,
And many a pleasant day we spent in the glens of Arralo [Aherlow].

My father died—I closed his eyes outside our cabin door—
The landlord and the sheriff were there the day before.
And then my poor old mother and my sisters three or so
Were forced to go with broken hearts from the glen of Arralo.

Bereft of home and kith and kin, and plenty all around,
I starved within our old cabin and slept upon the ground.
Then for three long months in search of work I wandered far and near,
I then went to the poorhouse to see my mother dear.

But the news I heard near broke my heart, but still, in all my woe,
I thanked the friends who dug their grave in the glens of Arralo.
But cruel as my lot it was, I never did hardship know
Till I joined the foreign army far away from Arralo.

'Rise up, there,' said the corporal, 'you lazy sleepy hounds!
Why can't you hear, you drowsy dogs, the call to army sounds!'
For as I have been dreaming of days so long ago,
But I woke before Sebastopol, but not in Arralo.

I grasped to get my musket, I thought how dark the night,
But, bless us all, it was not dark, it was the broad daylight;
And when they found that I was blind, the tears began to flow,
And I longed for just a pauper's grave in the glens of Arralo.

Now hearken, you dear countrymen, to what I have to say:
Though sorrow should befall you and misfortune come your way,
If ever you are tempted a soldier for to go,
Oh, think of Paddy Sheahan and the glens of Arralo.

Now a poor neglected mendicant I wandered through the street,
My nine months' pension being run out, I beg from all I meet;
But as I joined my country's tyrants, my face I'll never show
Amongst the kind old neighbours that lived in Arralo.

The first printed appearance of 'The Dying Stockman' was in
the *Portland Mirror* (8th July 1885), where it was signed C.A.F.
Apparently it was written one night at Gatton, Queensland, by
Horace Flower and his friend Walton Kent, as a parody of the
popular English song, 'The Tarpaulin Jacket'.

A strapping young stockman lay dying,
A saddle supporting his head;
And his comrades around him were crying
As he leant on his elbow and said:

CHORUS:
  Wrap me up in my stockwhip and blanket
  And bury me deep down below,
  Where the dingoes and crows will not find me,
  In the shade where the coolabahs grow.

Cut down a couple of saplings,
Place one at my head and my toe;
Carve on them a stockwhip and saddle
To show there's a stockman below.

There's some tea in that battered old billy,
Place the pannikins all in a row,
And we'll drink to the next merry meeting
In the place where all good stockmen go.

I hear the wail of a dingo
In the gloom of the scrubs down below,
And he rings the knell of a stockman.
Farewell, dear old pals, I must go.

If I had the wings of a pigeon
Far over the plains I would fly;
I'd fly to the arms of my loved ones
And there I would lay down and die.

Lance Skuthorpe, a third-generation Australian, born in the Kurrajong Hills of New South Wales, died in March 1957 at the age of eighty-seven years. He was famous as a buckjump rider and bush showman, best known, perhaps, as the only horseman other than Adam Lindsay Gordon to put a horse over the famed Gordon's Leap at Mount Gambier. He was not only a remarkable horseman, but showed a great talent for story-telling. 'The Champion Bullock Driver', his best-known effort, was buffed and polished in his mind for a long period before being committed to paper. Skuthorpe played several musical instruments and was also a good step-dancer.

Skuthorpe's son, also called Lance, and one daughter, Violet, carried on the family tradition in show business. His daughter Madge (Laver) inherited her father's love of singing bush songs, but could not remember the words of 'The Stockman's Last Bed' and referred Meredith to her mother, Violet Skuthorpe senior.

Violet senior is a daughter of Teddy King, a famous steeplechase jockey and later a Cobb and Co. driver and also a concertina player and singer of Irish and Australian songs, who lived most of his life in the Horsham district of Victoria. As well as 'The Stockman's Last Bed', two jockey ballads, 'Donald Campbell' and 'The Whip and the Spurs', were taken down from Violet senior's singing; all were learned from her father.

A text only slightly different from Mrs Skuthorpe's 'The Stockman's Last Bed' was printed in the *Bulletin* in 1888 under the title 'The Dying Stockman'; it had been learned by the contributor at the beginning of January 1865 while sailing from Wickham on the Lower Burdekin.

Mrs Skuthorpe sang 'Donald Campbell' very slowly and sadly. Most jockey ballads have rather banal tunes, but 'Donald Campbell' is an exception—a slow-moving, haunting tune that is strongly reminiscent of the American folk hymn 'Wayfaring Stranger'.

Chorus

Be ye stockmen or not, to my story give ear:
Alas, Jack has gone and no more shall we hear
The crack of his stockwhip, the steed's lively trot,
The clear 'Go ahead!' and his jingling quart-pot.

CHORUS:

    He sleeps 'neath the wattle
    In sweet perfumed shade.
    In the tall gumtree's shadow
    Is the stockman's last bed.

One day he was yarding, he was gored by a steer;
'Alas!' cried poor Jack. 'It's all up with me here.'
His whip shall be silent, and his dogs they will mourn,
And his steed looks in vain for his master's return.

Stranger, if ever in some future day
In search of wild cattle should you chance for to stray,
Tread light 'neath the wattle, where poor Jack is laid,
So far from his home where in childhood he played.

Once I loved a fair young jockey,
Donald Campbell was his name,
Until it pleased God for to take him,
Then a mourner I became.

CHORUS:

All his comrades, do take warning,
All his comrades, listen to me,
How he left for the course that morning
Never more his home to see.

He was riding a horse called Luna
In the Allforced Handicap;
He was thrown, his neck was broken
By a stump was on the track.

There he lay for three days after,
In his colours, most bright and gay,
Until a jury passed a verdict
Of accidental death that day.

THE WHIP AND THE SPURS

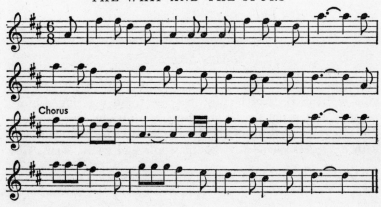

'One hundred pounds,' the master said,
  'To you, me boy, I'll pay
If you will win this race for me
In which you ride today.'

I looked him steady in the face,
And, touching the cap I wore,
Said I, 'I'll do my very best,
And a jockey can do no more!'

  And with the whip and the spurs,*
  And a pony to a pin,†
  If ever a jockey rode in a race,
  This day I ride to win.

She whinnied when I patted her,
For well my beauty knew
As well or better than myself
The work she had to do.

The first time round the course was run
In need of a steady, strong arm;
The mare began to fret and pull
And her blood began to warm.

And in the middle of the ruck
I passed them all but two,
And coming in the straight, me boys,
The mare she fairly flew.

  Then the whip and the spurs*
  I applied with all my strength,
  And as she answered, yes, me boys,
  I won it by half a length.

Gladys Scrivener

When John Meredith went to see Gladys Scrivener at Erskineville in 1956 she said bluntly that she could not sing. Unfortunately, it was not the usual case of 'mike fright' and although she was persuaded to try she was inclined to be tone deaf, yet with a perfect memory for both words and tunes. Transcrip-

* Mrs Skuthorpe only sings a chorus after verses 2 and 5.
† A £50 to £1 bet.

94

tions of her songs were not difficult to make because her habit of sharpening tones over certain intervals was a regular one.

Some of her songs were learned in childhood (the early 1920s) from her grandfather, more from her father, J. M. Power of Maitland, and others from her aunt who lives in the same town. Her father was born at Narrabri, New South Wales, in 1888 and spent most of his youth on the track as a shearer, but later became a railway ganger. Both her father and her grandfather had worked in the northern and north-western districts of New South Wales as drovers and in general bush work, and there they learned their songs.

Grandfather Power wrote down the words of songs in a large notebook which J. M. Power kept for many years. The weekend John Meredith set out for Maitland to interview and record Mr Power and his sister, the Hunter River came down in flood and he was unable to proceed beyond Newcastle. Even worse, the flood carried away the old notebook. When, eventually, Meredith did get to Maitland, Mr Power was suffering from a heart complaint and unable to sing, and his sister was ill with bronchitis.

J. M. Power did manage to recite a fragment of a bawdy version of 'Waltzing Matilda'—

> Down came a black gin to drink at the waterhole,
> Up jumped the swagman and grabbed her on his knee,
> Saying, as he put his hand on her tar-rar-rum-tum,
> 'You'll come a-waltzing matilda with me'—

and also a few verses of 'Nine Miles from Gundagai'—

> As I was walking down the road
> I heard a lady say,
> 'Here's Joe Rule, the bullocky bloke,
> He's bound for Gundagai.'
>
> Now Joe he was a manly chap,
> Would share his only crust,
> But a bigger bloody bastard
> Never drug a whip through dust.
>
> But Nobby fell and broke his yoke,
> Poked out the leader's eye,
> And the dog shit in the tuckerbox
> Nine miles from Gundagai.

The shearer's cook the shovel took
The damper to unfurl,
Another sod, so help me God,
It bangs the bloody world.

The sun shone in the driver's eyes
The wheel run in a rut,
The whip flew off the handle
And his dog flew up a slut.

There are several more verses to the recitation. Some versions give the distance as nine miles, some as five. One old chap said this was because there was once a bad boggy patch at the Five Mile Creek on the Sydney Road from Gundagai, and another bad stretch nine miles out on the road to Jugiong. The verses date back to the neighbourhood of 1850, and a fragment is quoted in a Gundagai newspaper of 1854.

The song 'Bound for Sydney Town', sung by Gladys Scrivener, roughly follows the words of a broadside ballad of 1828 called 'Botany Bay'. She said that after learning her present version she heard the American counterpart known as 'The Boston Burglar'.

BOUND FOR SYDNEY TOWN

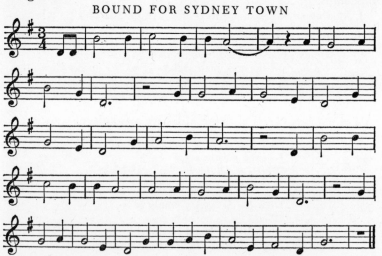

I was born in London city, boys, in a place I know full well,
Brought up by honest parents and the truth to you I'll tell;
Brought up by honest parents, boys, and reared most tenderly,
Till I became a wanderer lad at the age of twenty-three.

My character was taken and I was sent to jail;
My friends they tried to bail me out; it was of no avail.
The jury found me guilty and the clerk he wrote it down,
Saying, 'Now, my boy, for seven long years, you are bound for Sydney
  Town.'

I saw my aged father dear, pleading at the bar,
Likewise my poor mother was a-tearing of her hair;
She was tearing of her old grey locks and the tears came streaming
  down,
Saying, 'My dear son, what have you done that you're bound for
  Sydney Town?'

There's a girl in London city, boys, a girl I knew full well,
And if e'er I gain my liberty, it's along with her I'll dwell.
I'll give up all night walking and bad company I'll shun,
Likewise unto all rogues and roughs and the drinking of bad rum.

Oh, all young men at liberty, pray keep it while you can,
And when you walk the streets at night don't break the law of man;
For if you do, you'll surely rue, and be something like me,
A-serving out of seven long years in a penitentiary.

The ballad of 'Bold Jack Donahoe', learned by J. M. Power in
the bush in northern New South Wales about the turn of the
century, was passed on to his daughter. Gladys Scrivener said
she had heard her father sing 'The Wild Colonial Boy' to the
same tune.

BOLD JACK DONAHOE

In Dublin town I was brought up, in that city of great fame,
My decent friends and parents they will tell to you the same;
It was all for five hundred pounds I was sent across the main,
For seven long years in New South Wales to wear a convict's chain.

CHORUS:
  Now come along my hearties, we'll roam the mountainside,
  Together we will plunder and together we will die,
  We'll wander o'er the valleys and we'll gallop o'er the plains,
  For we scorn to live in slavery, bound down in iron chains.

G

I'd scarce been there twelve months or more upon the Australian shore
When I took to the highway, as I'd oft times done before.
There was me and Jacky Underwood, and Webber and Walmsley too—
These were the true associates of bold Jack Donahoe.

Now Donahoe was taken all for a notorious crime,
And sentenced to be hung upon the gallows tree so high.
But when they came to Sydney jail he left them in a stew,
And when they came to call the roll they missed Jack Donahoe.

Now Donahoe made his escape; to the bush he went straightway.
The people they were all afraid to travel night or day,
For every day the newspapers had published something new
Concerning this dauntless hero, the bold Jack Donahoe.

As Donahoe was cruising one summer's afternoon,
Listening to the mocking birds, their pretty laughing tune,
When the sergeant of the horse police discharged his carabine,
And called aloud on Donahoe to fight or to resign.

'Resign to you, you cowardly dogs, a thing I ne'er will do!
For I'll fight this night with all my might,' cried bold Jack Donahoe.
'I'd rather roam these hills and dales like a wolf or kangaroo
Than work one hour for Government,' cried bold Jack Donohoe.

He fought six rounds with the horse police until the fatal ball,
Which pierced his heart and made him start, caused Donahoe to fall.
And as he closed his mournful eyes, he bade this world adieu,
Saying, 'Convicts all, both large and small, say prayers for Donahoe.'

Mrs Scrivener knew a few of her grandfather's songs. He was
a shearer in the north-west districts of Narrabri and Moree. One
song that came from him was 'Bold Ben Hall'. The ill-treatment,
and especially the death, of Ben Hall was a favourite topic with
bush singers, probably second only to the Kellys in popularity.

BOLD BEN HALL

Come all Australian sons to me: a hero has been slain,
And cowardly butchered in his sleep upon the Lachlan plains.
Oh, do not stay your seemly grief but let a teardrop fall,
Oh, so many hearts will always mourn the fate of bold Ben Hall.

No brand of Cain ever stamped his brow, no widow's curse did fall.
When times were bad the squatters dread the name of bold Ben Hall;
He never robbed a needy chap, his records best will show,
He was staunch and loyal to his friends and manly to the foe.

Oh, and savagely they murdered him, those cowardly blue-coat imps,
Who were set on to where he slept by informing peeler's pimps.
Ever since the good old days of Turpin and Duval
The people's friends were outlaws too and so was bold Ben Hall.

This singer recorded songs about other bushrangers for John Meredith, including one on the Kelly brothers. Meredith's *Songs from the Kelly Country* includes a much longer ballad than is given here. While the tune used is Mrs Scrivener's, the words in that particular publication came from the late J. K. Moir, O.B.E.

This song is an obvious parody of Collins's lament for the drowned seafaring heroes of England.

YE SONS OF AUSTRALIA

Ye sons of Australia, forget not the brave,
And gather wildflowers to place on their graves.
They were four daring outlaws, their race it is run,
And we'll lay on their tombstones the laurels they've won.

To the banks of Euroa they made their first dash,
They cleared out its gold and they steered for the bush.
Black trackers and troopers on guard were at hand,
But they wiped out their enemies where'er they drew hand.

Now this gallant Kate Kelly was noble of mien,
She would sit on her horse like some new-born queen,
She would ride through the forest, revolver in hand,
Regardless of danger and errant of hand.

May the great god of angels protect as of old,
May her name be regarded in letters of gold.
Her brothers were outlaws, she loved them most dear,
And she hastened to tell them when danger was near.

'The story as I heard it,' said Mrs Scrivener before she sang 'Gallant Peter Clarke', 'was that Peter Clarke and Jimmy Clarke (who were not related) had camped on the banks of the Page River, and were attacked by an unidentified robber. Peter Clarke made an effort to seize the robber's gun, while Jimmy sought help from the camp they had left. When he returned, he found that Peter Clarke had been shot dead, but in dying had not relaxed his hold on the assailant's throat, and so had prevented him from escaping.'

GALLANT PETER CLARKE

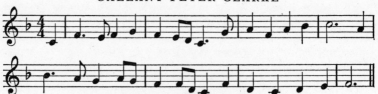

On Walden's Range at morning time
The sun shone brightly down;
It shone across the winding Page
Near Murrurundi town.

It glittered o'er the Burning Mount,
Where murky shadows fell
Across a path to travellers known
To some, alas, too well.

There stands a simple block of stone,
Erected as a mark
To show the spot where he fought and died,
That gallant Peter Clarke.

And if you will but list awhile,
To you I will relate
What happened there to Peter Clarke
And Jimmy Clarke, his mate.

100

They camped one night close by the range,
In songs the hours flew past,
And little did poor Peter think
That night would be his last.

At dawn they toiled the steep ascent;
They had scarcely reached the top
When a voice in accents stern and cold
Commanded them to stop.

'Hand up your money, watch and chain,'
The robber sternly cried.
'Who takes my money takes my life!'
The angry Clarke replied.

Then laughed the robber loud in scorn
As he his pistol drew.
Said he, 'My hand is firm and strong,
And my aim is ever true.

'And he who will my word gainsay,
Though he be earl or knight,
I swear by all I sacred hold
He ne'er shall see morning light.

'So give up your money now, my lad,
And do not idly rave.
Resist and, by the God above,
This night you'll fill the grave.'

'Those are but words and idle words,'
The daring Clarke replied,
And with one rapid bound he strode
Close by the robber's side.

And now commenced the struggle
For life between them both,
One hand of Clarke's the pistol grasped
And the other grasped his throat.

Now haste you, haste you, Jimmy Clarke,
And seek for help in need—
Your comrade's welfare, nay, his life
Depends on your good speed.

But hark to that loud pistol shot,
In a second rends the skies.
A human being on the sod
In his death struggle lies.

But in his dying gasp
Poor Peter seemed to say,
'Revenge, revenge you, Peter Clarke!'
And so he passed away.

But the robber, frightened by his deed,
In terror now did lie,
For the hand of Clarke upon his throat
Is tighter as he died.

And so indeed was he revenged,
For God has said it so—
'Who takes a life must yield a life!'
And the murderer met his doom.

The same tune was used by Gladys Scrivener for 'The Cry "Look Out Below!"' and 'When Carbine Won the Cup', of which she could recall only a few lines:

A better race for the weight and pace
Has never been put on
Than what was done by Musket's son
In the eighteen-ninety Cup.

'The Cry "Look Out Below!"' is one of several goldfields songs written by Charles Thatcher which passed into the oral tradition. Sally Sloane, when living at Lithgow, sang Meredith a verse of this—localized for the New South Wales alluvial fields on the Lachlan—to a variant of the 'Gallant Peter Clarke' tune:

And when he came to the Lachlan
His heart was in a glow,
To hear the sound of the windlasses
And the cry 'Look out below!'

A complete set of words was later obtained from a friend of Sally Sloane, Ida Fielding of Dripstone.

WHERE'S YOUR LICENCE?

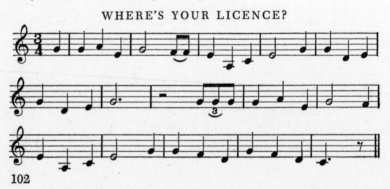

The morning was fine, the sun brightly did shine,
The diggers were working away,
When the inspector of traps said, 'Now, my fine chaps,
We'll go licence-hunting today.'

Some went this way, some that, some to Bendigo Flat,
And a lot to the White Hills did tramp,
While a lot more did bear towards Golden Square,
And the rest of them kept round the camp.

Each turned his eye to the holes he went by,
Expecting down on them to drop,
But not one could they nail, for they'd given leg bail—
Diggers ain't often caught on the hop.

The little word 'Joe' which all of you know
Is a signal that the traps are quite near—
Made them all cut their sticks and they hooked it like bricks,
I believe you, my boy, no fear.

Now a tall, ugly trap espied a young chap
Up the gully cutting like fun,
So he quickly gave chase, but 'twas a hard race—
I assure you the digger could run.

Down the hole he went, pop! whilst the bobby up top
Says, 'Just come up!' shaking his staff.
'Young man of the Crown, if you want me, come down,
For I'm not to be caught with such chaff.'

Now some would have thought the sly fox he'd have caught
By lugging him out of the hole,
But this cruster, no fear, quite scorned the idea
Of going underground like a mole.

But, wiser by half, he put by his staff
And, as onward he went, said he,
'When a cove's down a drive, whether dead or alive,
He may stay there till Christmas for me."

'That's a parody on "The Gay Cavalier",' was Mrs Scrivener's comment. She went on to sing a second parody to the same tune, a music-hall song called 'Rock-a-bye Baby'. Like 'The Cry "Look Out Below!"', 'Where's Your Licence?' was written by Charles Thatcher; it appears in several of his songbooks and was printed as a broadside in 1854.

103

Gladys Scrivener's final song was the rallying cry of the 'Wobblies' or Industrial Workers of the World (I.W.W.).

WORKERS OF THE WORLD

Fellow workers, pay attention
To what I'm going to mention,
For it is the fixed intention
Of the workers of the world.
And I hope you will be ready,
True-hearted, brave and steady,
To gather round the standard
Where the red flag is unfurled.

Now, the gunny-sack contractors,
They've all proved dirty actors
And they're not our benefactors,
As everybody knows;
And why their mothers reared them,
Or why God ever spared them,
Is a question we can't answer,
We, the workers of the world.

'I can't remember all that,' said Mrs Scrivener. 'That's "The River Fraser",' and went on to sing it:

Where the River Fraser flows
Each fellow worker knows,
They have bullied and oppressed us,
But still our union grows;
And we are going to find a way, boys,
Shorter hours and better pay, boys,
And we're going to win the day, boys,
Where the River Fraser flows.

Mrs Fraser-Paterson

One day, during a train journey to a picnic, a crowd of young men and women were having a singsong. Mrs Fraser-Paterson, who was sitting behind them, leaned over to say how much she enjoyed the old bush songs they had sung. Subsequently, Alan Scott and John Meredith visited her at Kogarah with their tape-recorders.

Her repertoire consisted of three songs which she said had been learned from her brothers when they were schoolchildren, that is, about 1910. Because her tune is somewhat different from the usual, her incomplete version of 'The Old Bark Hut' is included here.

THE OLD BARK HUT

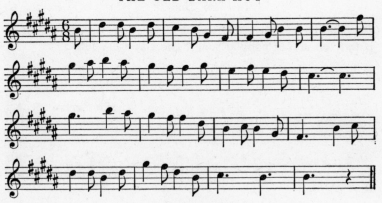

My name is Larry Dolan, I am an Irishman;
I'll sing you a song, my erring boys, to please you if I can.
Once I was well to do, but now I am stumped up,
And obliged to go on rations in the old bark hut.

Eight pounds of flour, twelve pounds of beef, a little sugar and tea,
That's all you'll get in Queensland until the seventh day.
You'll have to be mighty sparing, or you'll go with a hungry gut,
Which is one of the great misfortunes of the old bark hut.

The billy I boil my beef in, I carry my water too,
And you would think me mighty flash if I should ask for two.
A billy and a pint-pot, a broken-handled cup,
Sure, that's all adorns my table in the old bark hut.

The seat that I sit upon is but an old gin case,
[Line missing]
It serves me as a safe too, but I have to keep it shut,
Or the flies would do a canter round the old bark hut.

I make my bed down by the fire, and there I lay me down;
I think myself as happy as the king that wears a crown.
But when I'm going off to sleep, the fleas they wake me up,
And I curse and scratch with vengeance in the old bark hut.

And now, young ladies here tonight, don't think my language rude,
[Line missing]
And children too, when you grow up,
Please remember Larry Dolan in his old bark hut.

Jim Bourke

Jim Bourke of Surry Hills sang 'The Gun Canecutter' as a
parody on an old popular song, 'The Gay Caballero'.

THE GUN CANECUTTER

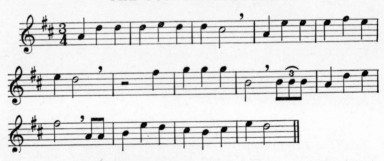

I am a struggling canecutter,
I rose right up from the gutter;
There's no joy for me,
I got to cook my own tea,
So I think I will marry a slutter.

Now, strolling home every night to my hutter,
To the wife of this gun canecutter,
I must have a jane,
Who'll help me cut cane,
One that won't stick the knife in her feeter.

Now in the slack I will meet her,
With tales of my life I will greet her;
She'll look into me eyes,
She'll fall for my lies,
She's the wife of a gun canecutter.

In reminiscing about his canecutting days, Jim recalled a few lines of a song dealing with Weil's disease. 'The Weil's disease was a big strike in northern Queensland,' he said. 'The song runs—

We sacked the cook, and a good job too,
Because we wouldn't have seen the season through;
For the first three weeks he fed us half-cooked rice,
And now he's got the cheek to feed us Weil's-diseased mice . . . .

That's as much as I know of it.'

The stanza actually belongs to a fairly long piece called 'On the Banks of the Isis River' or 'The Canecutter's Lament', another verse of which reads:

I cut cane, in Queensland,
On the banks of the Burdekin River,
The cook was mad, the grub was bad,
And the boss had shit on the liver.

During its life, this song has gathered a few lines from Lawson's bawdy song, 'The Shearer's Lament'.

Jim Bourke's second song concerns timber-getting in Queensland. He also sings a fragment of 'Australia's on the Wallaby' to a variant of the same tune, which, in turn, is very similar to that used in northern Queensland for Henry Lawson's 'Freedom on the Wallaby'.

Bourke told John Meredith something of the background to the timber-getting song. He said, 'It was written near Ravenshoe. It was made up by Paddy McMahon.' He went on, 'I was camped at Vine Creek. We were cuttin' timber for a feller named Mazlim—he was the mill-owner there—and layin' on the bunk, and it was rainin' and we couldn't get the timber in.' And so 'Mazlim's Mill' was composed.

(In this song 'double bank' means to yoke two teams of bullocks in tandem, while 'the balance due' is that part of the contract money held back by the employer to ensure that a job is completed satisfactorily.)

Now I am a bullock driver and I work for Mazlim's Mill,
And pulling timber from Vine Creek I've nearly had my fill.
And when the rain it comes at last, the roads they are like glue;
It's dig her out, or double bank, to find the balance due.

The cutters are no better off, at us they cannot grin,
For when they get their timber cut, they cannot get it in;
And my advice to you, my boys—please do not take it ill—
Far better turn your bullocks out than work for Mazlim's Mill.

Jim Parker

Jim Parker was born at Clunes, Victoria, in 1876, and spent his early youth at Broken Hill rabbiting and carting water, and around Bourke, where he did some droving. When working in Western Australia at a later date, he was a carrier and labourer on the boilers and condensers distilling fresh water for the mining towns of Coolgardie and Kalgoorlie. On the move again, Jim Parker went to Queensland and met his wife, Margaret (*née* Brennan), whose mother immigrated from Tipperary. Her father, John Brennan, was Irish-Australian.

Jim Parker was the first teamster to cart coal from Collinsville, Queensland, to the railhead at Bimby, ten miles away. After the railway came right to Collinsville, he changed to general carrying with his horse team, later owning the first Ford truck in the district. He died in 1954.

Jim Parker sang 'When the New York Boat Comes Down' to an American Civil War tune, 'Jubilo', or 'The Day of Jubilo'. The song was localized in Australia, and in 1956 Bill Wannan printed a fragment in the *Australasian Post*, sent in by Mr H.

Hearnden of Gordon, New South Wales, an ex-paddle-boat worker of the early 1900s. A drinker in a Morgan pub sang—

> *The smoke went up the chimney-stack,*
> *And the wheels went round and round,*
> *So fare thee well, my pretty little girl—*
> *And the good old boat went down.*

CHORUS:

> *Oh, the Bundaberg is a very fine boat,*
> *And a very fine captain too;*
> *He stands on top of the hurricane deck,*
> *And speaks his mind to the crew.*

The American song recorded by Parker was complete.

WHEN THE NEW YORK BOAT COMES DOWN

> *The summer air is bright and clear,*
> *The sky is fresh and blue;*
> *I won't stop, dear, to be very long here,*
> *To fool with a girl like you.*
> *Your eye is bright and your step is light*
> *And you won't say yes or no!*
> *There's lots of girls down Louisiana*
> *And it's down there I must go.*

CHORUS:

> *The smoke goes up the chimney-stack,*
> *And the wheel goes round and round;*
> *Fare you well, my curly-headed girl,*
> *When the New York boat comes down.*

109

The captain of the Glenby Rug
A very good man is he;
They say before he came on the river
He spent a short time at sea.
He's got a lovely voice he has,
And he loves to hear it sound,
He doesn't give a curse if the boiler bursts,
So long as the wheel goes round.

The engineer, you need not fear,
He keeps one eye on the beam,
With the deckboy sitting on the safety valve
To keep from losing steam.
He gives a scream with the whistling steam
Which scares the humming bee,
And the possum and the 'coon when they hear the tune
Step up in a neighbouring tree.

Mrs. Parker and her sister, Mrs. Sprike of Erskineville, sang 'The Bullockies' Ball', which they learned from their father; he picked it up while droving in the Gulf Country of northern Queensland. John Brennan, as well as singing bush songs at Bimby socials, was famous locally for his rendition of 'Brennan on the Moor'. 'The Bullockies' Ball' is a parody on the Irish ballad 'Finnegan's Wake', and is typical of a whole series of Irish comic songs that start with a celebration and finish in a free-for-all fight.

THE BULLOCKIES' BALL

The teams were camped along the gullies, soon the news flew round
about;
Plans were worked out by Pat Skulley; we gave the boys a grand
blowout.
We had an awning of tarpaulin, kegs and casks came quickly rolling;
Then the boys and girls came strolling to have a burst at the bullockies'
ball.

CHORUS:
Oh, my hearty, that was the party—help yourself, free gratis all.
Lots of prog and buckets of grog to swig away at the bullockies'
ball.

First came Flash Joe, but Jimmy was flasher, Hoppin' Billy, the one-
eyed boss,
Brisbane Sal, and the Derwent Slasher, Billy the Bull, and Paddy the
Hoss,
Nanny the Rat, the real macassar, Brisbane Bess and Mother McCall—
All came rolling up together to have a burst at the bullockies' ball.

Soon pint-pots began to rattle; the cry was, 'Pass the rum this way.'
The boys began to blow their cattle, the ladies of course must have
their say.
Sal said she'd take cheek from no man, and down to a dish of hash
did stoop;
She got a smack in the eye with a doughboy, put her sitting in a
bucket of soup.

Oh then, boys, there was the ructions—man the tucker and let fly.
Brisbane Bess with a hunk of damper caught Flash Joe right in the eye,
Nanny the Rat, the real macassar, with a frying pan a dozen slew;
She got a clip with a leg of mutton, took a dive in an Irish stew.

Waddurang Doughy Roley Foley said he'd put them to the rout,
Seized a junk of roly-poly, but a poultice of pigweed stopped his
mouth.
Now this raised his old woman's dander, and into an awful tanter flew;
'Fair play!' cried she to a bleeding overlander. 'You pumpkin-peeling
toe-rag snob!'

LAST CHORUS:
Oh, me hearty, that was the party—help yourself, free gratis all.
Blackened eyes and broken noses, that wound up the bullockies'
ball.

John Meredith also recorded a stanza and a half of the song
from Mr Thornton of Castle Hill, a Sydney suburb.

There was Billy Maloney's brother, and his cousin Jacky Small,
Always fighting one another, doing their best to stop the ball.
Up jumped Mrs Michael Foley; said, 'Those two, I'll chuck them out!'
As she raised her hand to douse him, a poultice of pork clapped o'er
*   her mouth.*

[2 lines missing]
This raised the old woman's dander, as a spud bounced off her jaw,
With the pumpkin-peeling toe-rag mob she swore that she would
*   booze no more.*

(In this glorious brawl, 'prog' is food, 'waddurang' means old
woman or old-woman-like. The pigweed mentioned is a species
of portulaca which was boiled or eaten raw as a green vege-
table to prevent 'Barcoo rot' or scurvy.)

Jack Jackman

Only one complete song was collected from Jack Jackman of
Parramatta—a very old English folk song that also exists in this
country in a number of variants. Jackman, who is a compara-
tively young man, learned 'The Derby Ram' from Jim Bennett,
who died in 1929 at the age of eighty-nine.

THE DERBY RAM

As I was going to Derby,
'Twas on a Derby day,
I saw one of the finest rams
That ever was fed on hay.

> *Hi wrinkle Derby, winkle tooral-lay,*
> *Winkle tooral-laddie, winkle tooral-lay.*

This ram he had a tooth, sir,
That held four bags of corn;
You could drive a coach and four
In the inside of his horn.

His wool grew up so high, sir,
It reached up to the moon;
A man went up in May, sir,
And never came back till June.

The man who owned this ram, sir,
He must 'a' been awful rich,
And the man who told the story, sir,
Was a lying son-of-a-bitch.

Four texts and tunes for the song known as 'The Derby Ram' or 'The Old Tup' are given in Broadwood and Fuller Maitland's *English County Songs*. All these versions are quite different from the ones collected from Jackman, Carlin, and Linigen in Australia.

It was Jim Bennett who told Jackman a story about the Donahoe Cave on the Parramatta River. He said it had always been known by that name or as the Bushranger's Cave. According to legend, Donahoe occasionally used the cave as a camping spot and was supposed to have hidden money and other plunder there. Bennett also said many considered that Donahoe's accomplice—William, Jacky or Darky Underwood—because of his very dark complexion, was a half-caste aboriginal.

Jackman sang two fragments of songs for Meredith. First 'Botany Bay'—

> *Now, all you lads, come and listen*
> *To the words I'm a-goin' to say:*
> *Beware of the bulls and the barnacles,*
> *'Cause you're bound for Botany Bay.*

Then 'Five Miles from Gundagai'—

> *As I was going through Mooni Gap,*
> *I heard a maiden cry,*
> *'There goes Bill the Bullocky,*
> *He's bound for Gundagai.'*

H

The place mentioned in the first line varies from Conroy's Gap, Talbingo Hill, and Rocky Flat to just 'down the road'.

Charles Ayger

Mr Ayger of Glebe was aged seventy-nine when John Meredith recorded his singing in March 1957. Many of his songs were incomplete. Some he had learned at Geurie, near Wellington, New South Wales, and others while working in the bush, mostly in North Queensland. Several he had written himself.

A song variously known as 'The English Miner' or 'The Coolgardie Miner' was titled 'Castles in the Air' by Ayger. A song of the same name appears in several collections, American and European. H. K. Johnson (*Our Familiar Songs*) gives a text by J. Ballantine, composer unknown, while *Folk Songs of Europe*, edited by R. P. Whitehead, prints a European version.

The singing of 'The Shearer's Dream' as a traditional ballad is featured in Henry Lawson's short story of the same name in his book *Send Round the Hat*. While it seems doubtful that Lawson would use his own verses in this way, it is likely that he merely polished up an existing ballad. If he did write the verses, it must have been during his youth, for Charles Ayger (born in 1877) learned the song while still at school in Geurie, at a time when Lawson would have been no more than nineteen years of age. Ayger said that the air to which it was sung was 'The Saxon Tongue'. A closer study of the two showed a definite resemblance to 'Castle Gardens' which, as already mentioned, is the air used by bush singers for 'The Backblock Shearer'.

'The Shearer's Dream' was widely sung at the turn of the century; another version was contributed by 'Duke' Tritton (though this is not recorded here). The things mentioned in the song as fantastic are, of course, no longer so—shearers' quarters are today universally equipped with spring mattresses and pillows, some sheds have electric power plus fans, and for several years now, in New Zealand, Maori girls have been working in shorts as rouseabouts.

Ayger could not recall the second verse of the song about Mirabeau's racing win. He said it was sung to an old army marching tune from the Peninsular War and it is almost identical with Jack Luscombe's tune for 'Sam Griffith'.

114

The scene was in Australia,
And in the lonely bush
A prospector was sitting
Who'd just came to the rush.
His head was resting on his hands,
His thoughts had backward turned,
For scenes in dear old Ireland
His heart in hunger yearned.

CHORUS:
He was thinking of home, sweet home,
Far away o'er the restless foam,
He thought of the wife he had left behind,
He thought of his father and mother so kind,
And each boyhood friend he knew,

In fancy he saw there,
As in that far-off lonely bush
He built his castles in the air.

And as he sat and pondered
No sound fell on his ear;
A savage foe with deadly aim
At him had hurled a spear.
Cut down amid his fancies bright,
In death they found him there;
'Twas thus he died while still he built
Bright castles in the air.

THE SHEARER'S DREAM

Oh, I dreamt I shore in a shearin'-shed, and it was a dream of joy,
For every one of the rouseabouts was a girl dressed up as a boy—
Dressed up like a page in a pantomime, and the prettiest ever seen—
They had flaxen hair, they had coal-black hair—and every shade be-
tween.

CHORUS:

There was short, plump girls, there was tall, slim girls, and the
handsomest ever seen—
They was four-foot-five, they was six-foot tall, and every height
between.

The shed was cooled by electric fans that was over every chute;
The pens was of polished mahogany, and everything else to suit;
The huts had springs to the mattresses, and the tucker was simply
    grand,
And every night by the billabong we danced to a German band.

Our pay was the wool on the jumbucks' backs, so we shore till all
    was blue—
The sheep was washed before they was shore (and the rams was
    scented too);
And we all of us wept when the shed cut out, in spite of the long,
    hot days,
For every hour them girls waltzed in with whisky and beer on trays!

There was three of them girls to every chap, and as jealous as they
    could be—
There was three of them girls to every chap, and six of them picked
    on me;
We was draftin' them out for the homeward track and sharin' them
    round like steam,
When I woke with my head in the blazin' sun to find 'twas a shearer's
    dream.

MIRABEAU

You may talk of equine heroes
From Ajax to Grand-van-Ur,
Blair Athol, West Australia,
Any many a dozen more.
But there's one more worthy of a song
Than all the cracks I know,
I think with me you'll all agree,
In Johnson's Mirabeau.

The race is three parts over,
Now the backers must confess,
Their fancy, she is leading,

Showing signals of distress.
Orator is a-hard on her
As down the sward they go.
But what is this a-coming now?
By jove! It's Mirabeau!

'Won by a length!' the judge proclaimed;
Fred Rightwell rode her grand.
Some looked disappointed
As they came from off the stand;
They claimed her win was but a fluke,
But the bookies they can show
That someone knew the true value
Of Johnson's Mirabeau.

Bill Foster

John Meredith had a brief interview with the Foster family while visiting friends in North Sydney. He was taken around to see them by Joy Durst, a Sydney folk-singer and folk-lorist, who later helped establish the Victorian Bush Music Club; she died in 1965. At the Foster's Meredith recorded young Bill singing a song he had learned while on the track during the depression.

THE DYING BAGMAN

A strappin' young bagman lay dyin',
With his nose-bag supportin' his head;
All around him his cobbers were cryin'
As he rose on his elbow and said:

CHORUS:
> *Wrap me up in my old police blanket*
> *And bury me deep down below,*
> *Where the coppers and squatters can't touch me,*
> *In the shade where the old rattler blows.*

There's tea in the battered old billy,
The pannikins lie in a row,
So we'll drink to this last merry meetin'
Of bagmen before I go.

The father sang a version of 'Travelling Down the Castle-reagh' and recited the favourite piece of the bush reciter, 'The Stockman's Tale' or 'My Brother Ben and I'.

Jamie Carlin

Carlin, born near Red Cliffs, Victoria, in 1937, is one of the younger folk-singers who have consciously sought the oral tradition. In turn, he has been greatly influenced in his singing by his study. He plays the concertina and has a quick ear for picking up a tune. Periodically, when he has learned a new song from somebody, he calls on John Meredith to record it.

His father, descended from Irish stock, came to Australia from Greenock, the port of Glasgow, about 1924, and took to the bush during the depression a few years later. He worked his way north to the Gulf Country of Queensland, then south along the Darling River to Mildura, where he married and raised a family.

As far as it is possible to ascertain such a matter, 'The Little Fish' is Portuguese in origin, and is fairly widely known in North Queensland. Jamie Carlin learned it from Dick Fitzgerald, a ringer from Charleville, Queensland. Jack Wright of Coogee also sang some verses of the same song.

THE LITTLE FISH

There's a song in my heart for the one I love best,
And her picture is tattooed all over my chest.

119

> *Yea-ho little fish, don't cry, don't cry,*
> *Yea-ho little fishy, don't cry, don't cry.*

> *The ship's under way and the weather is fine,*
> *The captain's on the bridge hanging out of the lines.*

> *Little fish, when he's caught he fights like a bull whale,*
> *As he threshes the water with his long, narrow tail.*

A. L. Lloyd wrote in *The Singing Englishman* (p. 28) of some survivals among songs. 'You can still hear the songs from the old days that once had a deep magical meaning and were songs of the adoration of other animals than the Holy Lamb and pretty certainly these songs too, like the song of the Great Wren, were sung when the witches met up in the moonlit hills and danced around the Master.'

However, said Lloyd, 'Things change very much and instead of being dark and sinister many hymns in praise of the monstrous animals are now just dirty songs for a truckload of troops to sing, like the well-known *Derby Ram*. Though perhaps things have not altered that much after all, for on the evidence of Lambert Danaeus and others these witchsongs were often rough to say the least, as I suppose one might expect songs praising a fertility god to be.'

THE DERBY RAM

As I strolled into Derby town,
'Twas on a market day,
It was there I saw the finest ram
That was ever fed on hay.

CHORUS:

> Me-I-wrinkle Derby-o
> Me-I-wrinkle day,
> Me-ingle-dingle Derby-o
> Me-I-wrinkle day.

This ram, he had two horns, me lads,
That reached up to the moon;
St Patrick went up in January
And didn't come down till June.

The wool upon his back, me boys,
It reached up to the sky,
And there the eagles built their nest,
I heard the young uns cry.

The wool upon his belly, sir,
It reached down to the ground;
It was cut off and sent to England;
It fetched a thousand pound.

The butcher that killed this ram, me lads,
Was up to his neck in blood;
The boy that held the basin, sir,
Was washed away in the flood.

It took all the boys in Derby town
To roll away his bones;
It took all the girls in Derby town
To roll away his stones.

And all the boys around the place
They gathered on the rise,
And there they kicked about his stones
For they are of football size.

The man that owned this ram, sir,
He must have been mighty rich;
The man that composed this song, sir,
Was a lying son-of-a-bitch.

Carlin also sang a version of 'Dennis O'Reilly':

DENNIS O'REILLY

Oh, me name is Dennis O'Reilly,
From Dublin town I came;
For to travel this whole world over,
I sailed far o'er the main.
With me pack all on me shoulder
And a blackthorn in me hand,
I'll be off to Philadelphia
Like a ramblin' Irishman.

Ron Manton

THE BANKS OF THE CONDAMINE

'Hark, hark, the dogs are barking.
My love, I must away,
For the lads they're all horse-breaking;
No longer can I stay.
I'm bound for the camp, my love;
'Tis many a weary mile
To join those jolly horse-breakers
On the banks of the Condamine.'

'Oh Willie, dearest Willie,
Don't leave me here behind
To curse and rue the day that
You ever learnt to ride;
For parting with my own true love's
Like parting with my life.
Why don't you be a selector
And I will be your wife?'

'I'll cut off all my yellow locks
And go along with you,
Put on a pair of moleskins
And be a rider too;
I'll cook and boil your billy while
At riding you doth shine,
And I'll wash your dirty moleskins
On the banks of the Condamine.'

'Oh, Nancy, dearest Nancy,
With me you cannot go,
For the boss has just gave orders—
No females there, you know.
Your delicate constitution's
Not equal unto mine;
Then you could not ride an outlaw
On the banks of the Condamine.'

'Now that's as far as I can get,' said Mr Manton when he had
finished singing, but his version is almost complete.

John Meredith met Ron Manton, who was then seventy, in
1958 at a concert given for old-age pensioners one night in
Erskineville by the Bush Music Club. After Gay and Alan Scott
had sung their version of the same song, Manton went back-
stage during the interval to tell them of his own song.

Born at sea when his parents were on their way to Australia,
Ron Manton was of Welsh-Irish extraction. The family settled at

Spring Hill, Queensland, which was then bush, and Papa Manton obtained work on the railways. When Ron reached the age of fourteen years he joined the Royal Australian Navy and served twenty-five years. Since his retirement he has lived in Sydney.

At a meeting subsequent to the one mentioned above he recorded for Meredith 'The Wild Colonial Boy', a variant that preserves the essentials of the theme in half the usual length.

THE WILD COLONIAL BOY

He was a wild colonial boy, Jack Doolan was his name,
He had poor but honest parents, he was born in Castlemaine.
He was his mother's only hope, his father's only joy,
But a terror to Australia was the wild colonial boy.

CHORUS:
    So come ye all, my hearties, we'll roam the mountain side;
    Together we will plunder and together we will die.
    We'll ride across the mountain-tops and gallop o'er the plains,
    We'll scorn to live in slavery bound down with iron chains.

One morning, very early, as Jack slowly rode along
The birds were singing merrily their all-bright morning song,
When up three mounted troopers came—Kelly, Davis and Fitzroy—
And shouted out, 'Surrender! Here's the wild colonial boy.'

'Surrender now, Jack Doolan! You see there's three to one.
Surrender in the King's name, you daring highwayman!'
Jack from his belt a pistol drew and flashed his little toy.
'I'll die but not surrender!' said the wild colonial boy.

124

Another song learned by Manton when he was barely seven years of age and retained in his memory was 'Humping Old Bluey'. A longer song of the same name was printed in one of 'Bill Bowyang's' *Bush Recitations* series, and under the title 'The Poor Bushman' it reappears with slight emendations in Stewart and Keesing's *Old Bush Songs*. The tune has been used for one of the ballads on the death of jockey Alec Robertson (see p. 150).

HUMPING OLD BLUEY

Humping old bluey it is a stale game,
And that I can plainly see;
You're battling with poverty, hunger, sharp thorn—
Things are just going middling with me.

Now the shearing's all over, and I'm such a swell,
I'm riding a very fine hack;
If my friends were to see me, I'm not humping bluey,
I'm pushing a bit further back.

Humping your drum, that after rum,
Wasting your young life away;
You're battling with poverty, hunger, sharp thorn—
Things are just going middling, I say.

When he came to record the song of 'Mrs McGrath', Ron Manton found he had lost several lines belonging between his first and second stanzas. However, a complete song was later provided by Sally Sloane. This Irish song is, wrote Colm O Lochlainn, 'Known to every true-born citizen of Dublin'. O Lochlainn's version is borne by a tune which, particularly in the chorus, closely resembles Ron Manton's, but the text is much the same as Sally Sloane's song, which she calls 'My Son Ted' (p. 197).

125

'Now, Mrs McGrath,' the sergeant said,
'Would you like to make a soldier of your son Ted?
With his thundering sword and his high cocked hat!'
'Now, my son Teddy, wouldn't you like that?'
With a doo-di-ay, doo-di-ay,
Doo-di-fol-the-diddle-doo-di-ay.

'Now, my son Teddy is tall and slim,
He has two joints in every limb;
He has two legs and they are small,
Well, divil damn the leg! Well, he's got none at all!'
With a do-di-ay, etc.

'Now were you drunk or were you blind,
When you left your two fine legs behind?'
'But a big cannon-ball on the fourth of May
It blew my two fine legs away.'
With a doo-di-ay, etc.

Collie Bourke

Mrs Bourke, who was living in Paddington when her singing
was recorded, learned 'The Old Bullock Dray' and 'Wild Rover
No More' from her father, one of the pioneers of Burragorang
Valley. The Bourke farm was resumed to make way for the
Warragamba dam, and is now submerged, but Collie Bourke
lived in the valley right up to the time the dam was constructed.

The only part of 'The Old Bullock Dray' which Mrs Bourke
could remember was the chorus, but as verse and chorus were
usually sung to the same tune the melody of her version suffices.

THE OLD BULLOCK DRAY

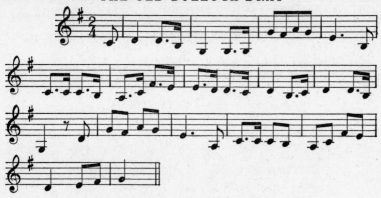

So roll up your bundle, and come and make a push,
I'll take you up to Narrabri and show you round the bush.
Such a chance, I'll be bound, you can't get any day,
So come and take possession of my old bullock dray.

WILD ROVER NO MORE

I've been a wild rover this many a year,
And I spent all my money on whisky and beer,
But now I'm returning with gold in great store,
And I never shall play the wild rover no more.

CHORUS:
> And it's no, no, never,
> Never no more,
> No, I never will play the wild rover no more.

I went to a shanty I used to frequent,
And I told the landlady my money was spent.
I asked her for credit, she answered me Nay,
Saying, 'Customers like you I can get any day.'

127

Then I drew from my pocket ten sovereigns bright,
And the landlady's eyes opened wide with delight.
Said she, 'I have whisky and wines of the best,
And the words that I uttered were only in jest.'

I'll go home to my parents, tell them what I have done,
And ask them to pardon their prodigal son,
And if they will do so as often before,
I never shall play the wild rover no more.

ALTERNATE CHORUS:
> Nay, no, never,
> Never no more,
> No, I never will play the wild rover no more.

Jack Wright

Like a large proportion of other bush singers, Jack Wright of the
Sydney suburb of Coogee had many songs from his parents. A
fine shearer's song, for example, was first learned by his father
when shearing at Garrawilla station near Moree. One day a
shed-hand made up the song and then distributed handwritten
copies to his hut mates.

GARRAWILLA

I sing of Garrawilla, a station of the glen,
Like a gem among the mountains, the home of gallant men.
I mean the jolly shearers, who there reside in peace,
And send to dear old England Australia's golden fleece.

CHORUS:

> *Oh, boys, a shearer's life is jolly,*
> *Oh, boys, a shearer's life is free,*
> *Oh, boys, a shearer's life's a jolly life,*
> *And a shearer's life for me.*

Now a shearer's life is not all joy, for weary days they pass
Thinking of their horses and looking out for grass.
The boss he makes them knuckle down, and if his sheep they scar
Lord help the man that does it if he calls not for tar.

If he would keep his tally up, a shearer cannot slack,
For sheep condemned as badly shorn have raddle down the back;
And wool it must come cleanly off, as all good shearers know,
And if you nick a pizzle then hump your drum and go.

And when the sheds have all cut out and shearing time is o'er
The shearer rolls his bluey up and moves along once more.
Some travel to their wives and homes, while others go to town,
And over wine and women they knock their money down.

And thus it is from year to year a shearer's life goes round,
Until the iron hand of Death it lays him in the ground.
But if up there in heaven they have a shearer's pen
You'll find that heaven's sheep are shorn by Garrawilla men.

Jack Wright was an interesting talker on the subject of nicknames:

'One of the cooks on the plains, the Liverpool Plains, was
known as Fol-the-diddle-di-doh,' he told Meredith. 'He earned
the name because he was always singing this song, "Fol-the-
diddle-di-doh". When any of the travellers—any of the swagmen—came to the men's hut or the kitchen for a hand-out, his
usual trick was to hand them the axe and sing:

> *'There's the axe and there's the wood,*
> *Fol-the-diddle-di-doh.*
> *When you think you've chopped enough*
> *Come and get a bit of duff,*
> *Fol-the-diddle-di-doh.*

'Another bloke had the name of Step-up. He used to walk

I

with a limp—a step-and-a-limp and a step-and-a-limp; so he got the name of Step-up.'

This fairly set him off. 'Then,' he said, 'there was Bob the Frog. Bob was in Coolamon and he was on the booze. He got in the horrors or something and took his clothes off and started to leap across the road like a frog. He was part aboriginal, and he looked a bit like a frog that way, so when he came out of boob he got the name of Bob the Frog.'

Wright laughingly told of the Baking-powder Cock. 'The Baking-powder Cock addressed everybody as "cock". And the story is—whether it's right or not—he stole some money and the only place he could hide it was in the baking-powder tin; so that's how he earned the name of Baking-powder Cock.

'And there was another bloke, Teddy Somebody, who always travelled with his brother. Teddy Cooper, that's right! When I met him he was always referring to "When Jack died . . ." so that it seemed that Jack had only died a little while ago, but someone told me that Jack had died years before. They were such good pals, these brothers, they were christened the Married Couple, because they always knocked about together.'

A variant of an Irish song, 'The Babies on the Block', sung by Ina Popplewell (but not included in this book), was the tune for Jack Wright's treatment of 'Jimmy Sago, Jackeroo'.

JIMMY SAGO, JACKEROO

If you want a situation and you'd like to know the plan
To get on a station, I'm just your very man.
Pack up the old portmanteau and label it Paroo,
With a name that's aristocratic—Jimmy Sago, Jackeroo.

When you get onto the station, and of small things make a fuss,
If you're speakin' of the station, mind, it's 'we' and 'ours' and 'us'.
Boast of your grand connections, and your rich relations, too,
And your own great expectations, Jimmy Sago, Jackeroo.

They will send you out on horseback the boundaries to ride;
Run down an old marsupial, and rob him of his hide.
His scalp will fetch a shillin' and his hide another two,
Which will help to fill your pockets, Jimmy Sago, Jackeroo.

When the boss wants information, on the men you'll do a sneak,
And don a paper collar on your fifteen bob a week;
And at the lamb-marking, the boss he'll make of you.
So that's the way to get on, Jimmy Sago, Jackeroo.

A squatter in the future, I have no doubt you will be,
But if the banks once get you, then they'll put you up a tree;
To see you humping bluey, I know will never do—
It would mean goodbye to our newchum, Jimmy Sago, Jackeroo.

'Sixteen Thousand Miles from Home' is another song received
by Wright from his father. In contrast to Edwin Goodwin, who
also sang this song, Jack Wright took it at a fast pace—if it is
sung as fast as the words can be formed the tempo will be
exactly right.

SIXTEEN THOUSAND MILES FROM HOME

131

Oh, I'm sixteen thousand miles from home
An' me heart is fairly achin'
To think that I should humble so
To come out here stone-breakin'.
The road I took was Bungreoo,
An' I met with a sub-contractor,
Who eyed me and studied me
As a parson or a doctor.
With me hooral-dooral
Tiddy falooral,
Tiddy-faloll-dee-i-doh.

Now I told him I was out of work
An' wanted some employment.
He sez, 'You do! You stink with scent!
You've had too much enjoyment!
Go over onto yonder hill,
Get from the boss a hammer,
An' nine an' six it is your pay,
An', mind you now, that's grammar!'
With me hooral-dooral, etc.

So I battered and whacked the whole of the day;
At evening I grew spiteful—
With the sight I didn't know what to do,
I hadn't broke me hatful.
Just then the boss he came along,
Sez he, 'You'll have to alter.
You'll be getting no run o' the store, be gosh!
You'll never make your salt, sir!'
With me hooral-dooral, etc.

So I chucked me hammer down on the heap,
With that I did consider,
I knocked the dust from off me boots,
An' battered me old black beaver.
Bad luck then to the mam an' dad
That reared me up so lazy;
With a silver spoon I'm a regular loon,
With hunger I'm very near crazy.
With me hooral-dooral, etc.

Now I'll go and 'list the army,
I'll go and 'list the rifle,
An' if I get shot I'll forget the lot,
All pastime and all trifle.
With me hooral-dooral, etc.

Before he sang 'The Little Fish' Wright said to Meredith: 'I got the song of "The Fish" off some Mediterranean fishermen, Portuguese, or Spaniards, or something, and they used to sing the song of "The Fish"—"Yo-ho little fishy, don't cry"—but they had a different version to what I heard you sing in the Church Hall. I heard it in North Queensland; I heard it in the bar, as a matter of fact. There were only two clean bits in it, and they are the bits I seem to have remembered—and that isn't because I've got a clean mind, either! They were the only two verses that stayed in my head, the two clean bits! I can give you those if you want them.'

Wright then sang—

THE LITTLE FISH

There are fish in the sea, there's no doubt about it,
Just as good as the ones that have come out of it.

CHORUS:
　　Yo-ho little fishy, don't cry, don't cry,
　　Yo-ho little fishy, don't cry, don't cry.

The crew are asleep, and the ocean's at rest,
And I'm singing this song to the one I love best.

He added, as he concluded, 'But where they come into the song, I'm not even sure of.'

Sid Heather

Sid Heather of Hurstville was a fiddler who accompanied him-self while singing. He was seventy-four when he recorded a number of dance tunes and one song for John Meredith. The song, 'The Wonderful Crocodile', was learned by his father on board a sailing ship bound for Australia. There are English and American versions.

In the year 1830 a Royal Navy brig, H.M.S. *Crocodile*, called at Sydney. The song may be a veiled satire on that vessel.

THE WONDERFUL CROCODILE

Come, all you lads, and listen to me;
To tell you the truth I'm bound:
What happened to me while going to sea
And the wonders that I found.
Shipwrecked I was at La Perouse
And cast upon the shore,
But I resolved to pick my way,
The country to explore.

CHORUS:
For I fal-the-ral the riddle of the ray-day
And fal the riddle of the ray-day.
For I fal-the-ral the riddle of the ray-day
And fal the riddle of the ray-day.

Now far I had not scurried out
When close alongside the ocean
I saw something move which at first I thought
Was all the world in motion.

But steering up along aside
I found 'twas a crocodile,
And from his nose to the tip of his tail
He measured five hundred miles.

This crocodile, I could plainly see,
Was not of the common race;
I was obliged to climb a jolly high tree
Before I could see his face.
And when he lifted up his jaws—
Though perhaps you'll think it a lie—
He reached above the clouds for miles three score
With his nose till he touched the sky.

While up aloft this tree so high
There blew a gale from the south;
I lost my hold and away did fly
Bang into the crocodile's mouth.
He quickly closed his jaws on me
And thought he'd grabbed a victim,
But I popped down his throat, you see,
And that's the way I tricked him.

I travelled on for a mile or two
Until I reached his maw,
Where I found rum kegs and not a few
And a thousand bullocks in store.
Of life I banished all my cares
For in grub I wasn't stinted;
I lived in this crocodile full ten years
And very well contented.

This crocodile was getting old;
Alas, one day he died.
He was three years in getting cold,
He was so long and wide.
His skin was ten miles thick, I'm sure,
Or somewhere near abouts,
For I was six months or more
In cutting my way out.

But now I'm safe on earth once more
Resolved no more to roam.
In a passing ship I got a berth
And now I'm safe at home.
And lest my story you should doubt—
If you ever travel near Blue Nile,
Just where he fell you'll find the tail
Of the wonderful crocodile.

Cyril Ticehurst

In his younger days Cyril Ticehurst of Kogarah Bay was a butcher at Grenfell, and it was there he learned his songs. Like Gladys Scrivener, he was inclined to be tone deaf, with a consistent flattening of notes in his singing. Most of his repertoire consisted of fragments, with one song, 'The Bright Shades of Blue', more or less complete. Several singers and musicians have sung or played fragments of the song, but Sally Sloane (whose version is not, however, included in this volume) is the only other singer to remember more than one or two verses.

THE BRIGHT SHADES OF BLUE

We had sailed in a vessel from Britain's cold shore;
I was treated unkindly, great chains that I wore.
My cares they were many, my joys they were few—
I'd left all my joys in those bright shades of blue.

Fair land of beauty, Australia so true,
How I sigh for those mountains in the bright shades of blue.
How well I remember that darkies' old song
That we sang round the fire, a once happy throng.

We had sailed in a vessel for Britain's brave shore;
I was treated with kindness, great jewels I wore.
But my cares they were many, my joys they were few—
I'd left all my joys in those bright shades of blue.

Fair land of beauty, Australia so true,
How I sigh for those mountains in the bright shades of blue.

136

Now I'm old and I'm feeble and my locks they are grey,
And the nearest and the dearest will soon fade away.

When I'm dead in my grave all I want you to do
Is plant me a gumtree from the bright shades of blue.
Fair land of beauty, Australia so true,
How I sigh for those mountains in the bright shades of blue.

Quite a number of people know a verse or so of 'Native Mate', but none have, so far, sung the complete song of four or five verses and chorus. Occasionally, the chorus does duty as the first stanza. In the Palmer-Sutherland collection of *Old Australian Bush Ballads* the chorus has been transferred to the 'Song of the Free Selector', to a different tune.

Ticehurst said, 'I don't know the first verse,' and went on to sing—

NATIVE MATE

CHORUS:

Build me a hut in my own native land,
Or a tent in Australia where the tall gumtrees stand;
I don't care how far back in the bush it may be,
With that dear native mate that will share it with me.

I like to be where the emu does stray,
And the wild native dog barks aloud for his prey,
Where the kangaroo and the wallaby and the wombats are there,
They are all to be found with the bandicoot and the bear.

Build me a hut in my own native land,
Or a tent in Australia where the tall gumtrees stand,
Or on the sea by Port Jackson, contented I'd be—
With the dear native mate that will share it with me.

It happens now and again that a singer forgets the words of a song completely, although the tune and theme of the ballad remain. Ticehurst, for example, knew portion of one of the forms of 'Dennis O'Reilly' or 'With My Swag All on My Shoulder', in the following piecemeal fashion:

TRAMP THE BUSHES OF AUSTRALIA

'First verse unknown. . . . Chorus:'

> *With my blankets on my shoulder*
> *And a billycan in my hand,*
> *I'll tramp the bush of Australia*
> *Like a true-born Irishman.*

'However, the singer met a girl, and—er—he got serious about it and the mother objected, and so she spoke to the daughter about it, and the chorus finished up with—'

> *Said the daughter to the mother:*
> *'I'll do the best I can,*
> *If I have to tramp the bush of Australia*
> *With my true-born Irishman.'*

Apart from the phrase, 'I'm sorry, mother [or father] died last year, we never bothered learning any of her songs', the words used by Ticehurst at the end of his fragment of 'Tom Corrigan' are the ones a collector dreads most to hear. Sometimes, months later in a sudden flash of recollection, the singer may remember several more verses, but more often nothing comes back.

TOM CORRIGAN

The flag had dropped and they had gone,
With Bondi in the lead,
When Corrigan on Waiter
Came on with mighty speed.
He was just outflanking Bondi
As they rounded on the turn,
When Waiter came a dreadful crash
And seemed to overturn.

And Corrigan fell beneath him,
With a deep wound in his head,
And all the people on the course
Thought Corrigan was dead—

'That's all I know of that. . . .'

Ticehurst was slightly more successful in recalling a localized treatment of 'The Boston Burglar', 'Bound for Charlers Town', 'Bound for Sydney Town', 'Botany Bay', or any other variants of the same song.

MORETON'S BAY

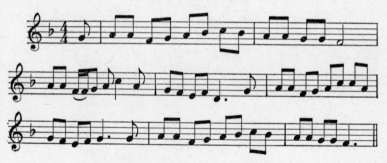

Come all you wild and foolish lads,
A warning take by me:
Never visit game-houses,
Or keep bad company.
For if you do, you'll surely rue,
And you will be like me,
[2 lines omitted]

For here I lie in Sydney jail,
My trial for to stand,
Expecting to be found guilty, lads,
And sent to a foreign land.

The jury found me guilty,
The judge to me did say,
'The jury finds you guilty, lad,
And we'll send you far away.'

We all set sail for Moreton's Bay
On a Sunday afternoon;
We reached on board the Vernon, lads,
On a Monday very soon.
And as those big ships they passed by
You could hear the sailors cry,
'There goes the gang of the forty thieves,
All bound for Moreton's Bay.'

One early printed version of 'Rub-a-dub-a-dub' or 'The Lime-juice Tub' gives the name of the air to which it was sung as 'The Rose Tree', which is, perhaps, more familiar to Australians as the tune for 'Goondiwindi'. Mr Ticehurst may not have had the correct tune, for he chants rather than sings.

RUB-A-DUB-A-DUB

With a pint of flour and a sheet of bark
We wallop up a damper in the dark.
With a roo-da-ma-ra,
And a rub-a-dub-a-dub,
Drive me back to the lime-juice tub.

You cockatoos, you never need fret,
For to show you up I'll never forget.

I'm the man that's game to bet
That you're over your head, heels first in debt.

Over your head, your neck as well,
And your daughters wear no crinolines.

Nor are they troubled with boots or shoes,
For they are wild in the bush with the kangaroos.
With a roo-da-ma-ra,
And a rub-a-dub-a-dub,
Drive me back to the lime-juice tub.

140

Bill Hughes

John Meredith first met Bill Hughes at a meeting of the Australian Folk Lore Society, and subsequently he recorded a number of genuine 'men's hut' songs which, unfortunately, cannot be printed in this book. As Hughes followed the usual round of the shearer, working through Queensland and New South Wales to Victoria, the songs have all of eastern Australia as their source.

Hughes sang a lively version of 'The Ryebuck Shearer' and had a fund of bush toasts, including one of which he remembered only four lines:

> Shearerman like toast and butter,
> Wolseley comb and Lister cutter;
> Rouseabout like plenty joke,
> Plenty rain, and engine broke.

The rhyme is supposed to have been written by an Afghan camel-driver, and is still well known in shearing sheds. The longer version given below was collected by Meredith from Dennis Ryan, who learned it in various Queensland and New South Wales sheds. Perhaps only four lines are really 'Shearerman', for parts have been heard sung at Holbrook to the tune of 'The Wearing of the Green'.

SHEARERMAN

> Shearerman like toast and butter,
> A Wolseley comb and a Cooper cutter;
> You can tell those greasy shearer bastards
> By the rags upon their feet:
> And when they see those speed balls,
> God Jesus! Can they eat!
> They shore wet sheep on Monday,
> And they shore them wet again,
> They make those poor old rousies work
> In ninety points of rain.
> The rouseabout he laugh and joke,
> Rains come down and engine broke.

Most bush toasts are recited, but Bill Hughes struck a new note by singing 'Little Bit of Sugar' to a primitive tune.

141

With a little bit of sugar and a little bit of tea,
A little bit of flour you can hardly see,
Without any meat, between you and me,
It's a bugger of a life, by Jesus!

Hughes sang 'The Dying Aviator' to the old 'Stalwart Young Lancer' or 'Tarpaulin Jacket' tune. In addition to 'The Dying Aviator', there is also a 'Dying Sleeper-cutter' (sung in the Gulgong district), and a 'Dying Harlot', the last, unfortunately, not printable. In England 'The Dying Aviator' is known, but it is sung to the tune of 'My Bonny Lies Over the Ocean'.

THE DYING AVIATOR

A young aviator lay dying
At the end of a bright summer's day;
His comrades around him had gathered
To carry his fragments away.

His airplane was piled on his wishbone,
His leevies was wrapped round his head,
He wore a spark-plug in each elbow.
'Twas plain he would shortly be dead.

He spat out a valve and a gasket,
And he stirred in the sump where he lay,
And to his wondering comrades
These few parting words he did say:

Take the manifold out of my larynx
And the butterfly valve from my neck,

Remove from my kidneys the cam-rods,
There's a lot of good parts in this wreck.

Take the piston rings out of my stomach
And the cylinders out of my brain,
Extract from my liver the crankshaft,
And assemble the engine again.

Pull the longeron out of my backbone,
And—'

'That piece is missing,' said Bill Hughes. 'However, he came to the gate, seeking admission to the fold. . . .'

'What have you done,' asked Saint Peter,
To be seeking admission up here?'
'Oh, I was a young air-force pilot
On earth for well over a year.'

The gate then moved open quite sharply
As Saint Peter touched a small bell.
He said, 'Come in and take up a harp, lad,
For you've had enough there of hell.'

The sentiment expressed in the first verse of 'Machine-guns They Rattle', as sung by Hughes, is much the same as in 'Sing Me to Sleep', another parody of the World War I period, sung by Arthur Buchanan (but not recorded here).

MACHINE-GUNS THEY RATTLE

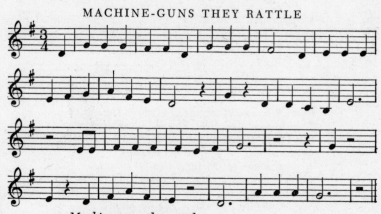

Machine-guns they rattle,
Jack Johnsons they roar,
I don't want to fight
With these Fritz any more.

Take me over the sea,
Where the Germans they can't get at me.
Oh, my, I don't want to die,
I want to go home.

Then Bill Hughes said, 'Now the bush version was:'

The engines they rattle,
The cutters they roar,
I don't want to shear,
These rough sheep any more.
Take me over the plain,
Where these rough sheep I won't see again.
Oh, dear, I don't want to shear,
I want to go home.

The last item in Bill Hughes's repertoire given in this book does not appear to be complete and was probably part of a music-hall ditty.

DOWN FELL THE OLD NAG

Down fell the old nag, dead between the shafts.
The old man said, 'Now the old nag's dead!
We'll have to pad it back to town.'
'Oh dear, no,' they all began to crow,
'It's much too far to run,
So we'll harness up the old woman
And put her in the shafts
And make her pull the whole lot home!'

Alec Hood

Alec Hood was an enthusiastic member of the Bushwhackers

144

group. He took a trip to Western Australia and met Toby Willis in the house where they both boarded. Hood heard Willis singing 'The Black Velvet Band' and obtained a copy of the words, at the same time memorizing the tune.

THE BLACK VELVET BAND

'Twas in the city of London,
In apprenticeship I was bound,
And many's the happy hour
I spent in that dear old town.
One day as I was walking
Along my usual beat,
A pretty little young maiden
Came tripping along the street.

CHORUS:

And her eyes they shone like diamonds,
I thought her the pride of the land.
The hair that hung down on her shoulders
Was tied with a black velvet band.

One day as we were walking
A gentleman passed us by;
I could see she was bent on some mischief
By the rolling of her dark blue eyes.

Gold watch she picked from his pocket
And slyly placed into my hand;
I was taken in charge by a copper . . .
Bad luck to that black velvet band!

Before the Lord Mayor I was taken,
'Your case, sir, I plainly can see,
And if I'm not greatly mistaken,
You're bound far over the sea.'
It's over the dark and blue ocean,
Far away to Van Diemen's Land,
Away from my friends and relations
And the girl with the black velvet band.

A second song learned from Toby Willis was another ditty of jockeys and horses:

THE JOCKEY'S LAMENT

The motto of our boys out here,
Who jockeys strive to be,
To mount our horse and scale the course,
The danger do not see.
There's one poor jockey's met his fate
Upon the Randwick course,
When he was thrown from off his mount,
That famous old black horse.

'Go, tell my poor old mother,
Who resides down in Geelong,
Go, tell her I've been injured
By those jockeys who run wrong.
My head is sore, my back is hurt,
I cannot stand the pain,
If God would only spare me
I'd never ride again.'

Delys Cross

A text, from the collection of Roland Robinson, of the following aboriginal song appeared in the Bush Music Club's magazine, *Singabout*, vol. 3, no. 3. It was collected along the northern coast of New South Wales. Delys Cross sang this version:

JACKIE JACKIE

> Jackie Jackie was a smart young fellow,
> Full of fun and energy,
> Yet he sat by the river of his people
> Underneath a great gumtree.
>
> CHORUS:
>   Krikita bubla well dee miah,
>   Billee niah ging gerrie wah.
>
> Jackie's people used to chase the emus
> With their spears and waddies, too.
> They were the only ones who could tell you
> What the emu told the kangaroo.
>
> White fella come and take Jackie's country,
> Spread their fences across his land.
> Now poor Jackie has to pay his taxes,
> And his hunting days are done.
>
> But the white man bring to Jackie
> Bottles of plonk and two-up game.
> Now the riverside re-echoes
> To their shouts as the pennies fall.

The last line of the chorus is sung very slowly.

Delys Cross of Caringbah, Sydney, heard the song at an aboriginal concert held in Melbourne about fifteen years ago. 'Jackie, Jackie', supposedly, had been specially composed for the occasion, but an aboriginal theological student now living in Sydney told John Meredith that he had learned the song at approximately the same time as Delys Cross while he was in Queensland. It could have circulated quickly, of course, but it seems likely the song is older than fifteen years.

Ben Castle

Ben Castle was in his seventies and living at Alexandria, Sydney, when John Meredith recorded him in 1959. Castle spent his childhood on a station in the Tarcutta district of New South Wales and when only ten years of age learned several songs from shearers about there. He learned 'The Wild Colonial Boy' in 1895, and although most of the text had been forgotten the tune was complete. Note that the phrase 'down in Castlemaine' refers to the Victorian township, 'down south' from New South Wales.

THE WILD COLONIAL BOY

The wild colonial boy, you know, Tim Doolan was his name,
Brought up by honest parents, reared down in Castlemaine.
He was his mother's hope and pride and his father's diamond joy,
And dearly did they love their son, that wild colonial boy.

The tune to which Ben Castle sang 'Are You There, Moriarity?' is a variant of Edwin Goodwin's 'Dennis O'Reilly' and, at the same time, almost identical with the fragment of a song sung by Sally Sloane called 'The Girl with the Flowing Hair'. Unfortunately, Castle remembered little in the way of words. Perhaps 'Moriarity' was known to people in the Kelly country before Ben Castle heard this song, since Max Brown in his book *Australian Son* quotes a satire on the police who were hunting the bushrangers:

148

The Kellys are having a mighty fine time
In the ranges not far away.
And we on their tracks think it mighty fine fun
To be doing nothing all day.

For our boss, the sergeant, is a very fine man,
And he lets us out, do you see;
So we settle in a shanty and we play forty-fives
And it suits Moriarity.

ARE YOU THERE, MORIARITY?

I'm a policeman sheikh or a pip or peak,
And the girls around my beat,
So nice and clean, they say, That's him,
As I go down the street.
I'm a handy feller at a custard,
I take it into custardy,
And the kids all cry as I go by,
Are you there, Moriarity?

In another instance, Ben Castle's words to a song show several interesting variations while his tune is practically identical with others printed in this book (see p. 54):

CASTLE GARDENS

Hurrah, my boys, our sails are set and the winds are blowing fair;
I'm bound for Castle Gardens, in a few weeks I'll be there.
And it's hard to part with the friends I love, and it fills my heart
*   with woe*
To leave the place my father built some fifty long years ago.

We owed the landlord three weeks' rent and I wished we owed him
     more,
For that day the village bailiff put the notice on our door.
And my poor old aged mother she would break her heart with woe
To leave the place my father built some fifty long years ago.

Two more songs by Castle concerned the jockey Alec Robertson. The first of the pair: 'Death of Alec Robertson', is identical in tune with Ron Manton's 'Humping Old Bluey' (p. 125), and a slight resemblance between that singer's 'Banks of the Condamine' and Castle's 'Wild Colonial Boy' can be observed.

DEATH OF ALEC ROBERTSON

A good man has gone, he's drawn his last breath,
Struck down in the midst of his pride.
Poor Alec Robertson met his sad death
On his favourite steed, Silvermine.

At the turn of the straights, so the story does tell,
Poor Robertson met his sad doom.
So mark the spot well, where poor Silvermine fell,
And the way that poor Robertson died.

The second song, a fragment, is simply given as 'Alec Robertson' and is almost the same, in both text and tune, as Edwin Goodwin's 'Arthur Nolan' (p. 65).

ALEC ROBERTSON

Dear friends, just listen for a while,
And a story I will tell.
It's about young Alec Robertson,
A bloke you all know well.

[Lines omitted]

Poor lad, his mother was not there
To bid him last goodbye,
While his stable-mate stood near
With a sad tear in his eye.

'I'm sorry that I let him ride . . .'

And here Ben Castle lost track of the words.

150

John Linigen

Seventy-five years old, John Linigen, a retired quarry-man, was born in, and has lived all his life in, St Ives, an outer suburb of Sydney. It took Mr Linigen forty years to cut the stone and complete the rambling house he lives in. He now spends his leisure hours carving small figures from sandstone.

John Linigen left school when thirteen to drive a horse and dray for the local council, then two years later went to a quarry in Cowan Road. Many years were spent working at the quarry and it was there he learned the songs he remembers.

In their early married days, he and his wife used to go by horse and sulky to Crows Nest for their supplies, Mrs Linigen driving. On these regular trips her husband entertained her by singing loudly all the way home. His repertoire, apart from a fragment of 'The Dying Stockman', consisted mostly of old music-hall and popular songs of the 1890s.

Linigen's version of 'Alec Robertson' was picked up from a boarding-house room-mate and is sung to the tune of 'The Jockey's Lament' as recorded by Alec Hood (p. 146).

ALEC ROBERTSON

Oh, the hobby of Australian boys
Is jockeying to be,
To mount a horse, to scale the course,
No danger do they see.
'Tis all very well just for a while,
Till the dreadful news goes home;
This is how a mother feels
When she finds she's lost her son.

Now it was the railing horse came down
With such a nasty fall,
On came old Silvermine behind,
Who scrambled over all.
The race was won by Expert,
And the jockey lay out dead,
And as they turned his poor head round,
These words he sadly said:

'Go and tell my poor old mother,
Who resides down in Geelong,
That I've been badly injured
By the jockey who rode wrong.

My head does ache, my sides do pain,
I feel I am insane.
If God would spare me for a while,
Till I see her face again!'

What most people refer to as 'The Wild Colonial Boy' was
'Jack Dowling' to John Linigen. His version is localized in the
Sydney suburb of Rooty Hill, once the hunting ground of Bold
Jack Donahoe, the original hero of this ballad.

JACK DOWLING

Oh, once there lived a highwayman, Jack Dowling was his name,
Brought up by honest parents, away down Castlemaine.
He was his father's only son, his mother's pride and joy,
And a terror to Australia was the wild colonial boy.

Now as Jack rode out one morning, as he merrily rode along,
Listening to some mocking birds, they sang their morning song,
Up rode three mounted troopers—Kelly, Davis and Fitzroy.
'Oh stand, oh stand!' cried Kelly. 'For there's three to one, me boy!'

'I'll fight but not surrender!' said the wild colonial boy.
Turning unto Kelly, he brought him to the ground,
He turned his gun to Fitzroy and gave him a deadly wound.
[Line missing]

[2 lines missing]
He turned his horse to the Rooty Hills and galloped across The Plain,
Singing, 'This is the way they captured the wild colonial boy.'

152

'Inky Dinky Derby Town' was John Linigen's name for a version of 'The Derby Ram', a song that makes several appearances in this book.

INKY DINKY DERBY TOWN

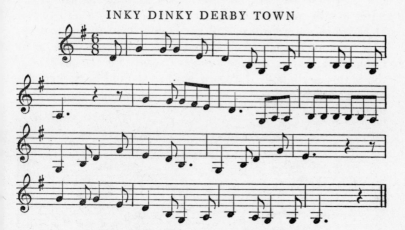

There was a ram of Derby town,
His horns were tipped with brass,
One grew out of his head, sir,
And the other grew out of his
Inky dinky Derby town,
Inky dinky day,
Inky dinky Derby town,
And Derby et the 'ay.

Now the man who owned this ram, sir,
He was very rich,
The man that proposed this story, sir,
Is a lyin' son of a
Inky dinky Derby town, etc.

Now this ram he grew a very fine fleece,
And it grew very thick,
Eventually it interfered
With the working of his
Inky dinky Derby town, etc.

Now this ram was used to jumping, sir,
He never made a fall,
He jumped a five-foot barb-wire fence
And tore off one of his
Inky dinky Derby town, etc.

Leo Dixon was working as a wharf-labourer when John Meredith met him. He had, however, spent most of his life in the bush, usually working as a shearer. Leo was born and reared at Eugowra, near the scene of the famous gold escort hold-up. The two songs given below and a fragment of 'The Wild Colonial Boy' were learned from his father. Leo Dixon played the button accordion, and knew most of the old favourites—the waltzes, varsoviennas, and schottisches, so popular among bush musicians.

ANOTHER FALL OF RAIN

Oh, the weather it's been sultry for a fortnight's time or more,
And shearers have been driving might and main;
And the boss is getting rusty and the ringer's caving in,
And his bandaged wrist is aching with the pain.

Oh, the clouds are driving eastward, the thunder's muttering low,
Oh, the clouds are driving eastward o'er the plain,
And I see the lightning flashing from the edge of yon black cloud,
And I hear the gentle patter of the rain.

154

So it's boys put on your stoppers, and let us to the hut,
We'll sit around and have a friendly game,
And while some are playing music, and there's some play Ante Up,
And there's others gazing sideways at the rain.

But now the storm is over, let the presser spring the screw,
While the teamster backs the wagon underneath. . . .

'And that's all I can remember of it,' said Leo.

The words of this were written by John Neilson of Penola, a bush worker, farmer, and balladist, and the father of Australia's greatest lyricist, John Shaw Neilson.

Dixon's only other song of any length was 'The Eumerella Shore'.

THE EUMERELLA SHORE

There's a happy little valley by the Eumerella shore,
Where I've lingered many happy hours away,
On my little free selection I have acres by the score,
Where I unyoke the bullocks from the dray.

To my bullocks then I say, no matter where you stray,
You will never be impounded any more,
For you're running, running, running on the duffer's piece of land,
Free-selected by the Eumerella shore.

When the moon has climbed the mountains and the stars are shining
    bright,
Then we saddle up our horses and away,
And we yard the squatters' cattle in the darkness of the night,
And we have the calves all branded by the day.

Oh, my pretty little calf, at the squatter you may laugh,
He will never be your owner any more,
For you're running, running, running on the duffer's piece of land,
Free-selected by the Eumerella shore.

If we find a mob of horses, and the paddock rails are down,
Though before they were never known to stray,
When the moon is up we drive them to a distant inland town,
And we sell them into slavery far away.

To Jack Robertson we say, we're on a better lay,
And we'll never go a-farming any more;
For it's easier duffing cattle on the little piece of land,
Free-selected by the Eumerella shore.

Herb Gimbert

Herb Gimbert was born at Newcastle, New South Wales, in
1888. He lived in Newcastle until about fourteen years of age,
then moved to Maitland to work in the Greta coalmines. While
on the Maitland field, he learned to play the tin whistle. A mate
of his used to play whistle to another friend's banjo accompaniment, so Herb taught himself to do the same. He had previously taught himself to play the mouthorgan when, as a boy,
he purchased a 'Bushman' model for 1s. 6d.; he had also learned
the accordion from his uncle, John Dillon, who played the
mouthorgan and accordion for old-time dances.

In 1923 Gimbert took up residence in Sydney.

This tune, now firmly established in Sydney as 'Herb's Jig', was learned from an old-time dance band featured in short-wave wireless broadcasts from St Kilda Town Hall, Melbourne, in the early 1930s. No doubt, in being transferred to the accordion by memorization, the tune acquired variations.

THE FLYING PIEMAN

The First Set Tune, used regularly by the Bush Music Club for a dance called 'The Flying Pieman', is really an Irish-reel tune that Herb learned from his grandmother, a Mrs Byrnes. She was born in Australia of Irish parents, and played a jew's-harp. Her father was a guard at Port Macquarie penal settlement in the colony's early days.

157

Part Two

Songs from west of the Blue Mountains— Lithgow, Mudgee, Gulgong

---

Bill Boundy

Bill Boundy of Lithgow is a talented musician in his early forties, playing most fretted instruments, string bass, and recorder flute. He and his mates are popular performers of musical variety acts at the Lithgow Workers' Club.

'Mary's Ass' is one of the songs he sings at the Club.

MARY'S ASS

You've asked for a story—I'll sing, I will tell,
About a young lady I knew very well;
Her name it was Mary, a beautiful lass,
And the song I will sing is about Mary's ass.

A present to Mary her uncle did make
That whenever she went to some exercise take
This donkey, or mule, he said, 'Sure, take your choice,
One that's gay and so frisky with beautiful voice.'

Now early next morning young Mary was out,
And all round the town was seen riding about.
'Twas the talk of the town, north, east, west and south,
In fact, Mary's ass was in everyone's mouth.
When tired of this, she would gallop back home,
Her ass would be covered with sweat and with foam;
She'd cry out to the groom, 'Grab a handful of grass,
Come down to the stable and wipe down my ass.'

Now old Joe, who sells greens, has a moke very old,
It is bony and lean from starvation and cold.
And whene'er he meets Mary, which often occurs,
How he wishes his ass was as handsome as hers.
Now early one morning as Mary did pass,
A lad with a straw slyly tickled her ass;
The mule gave a bolt, down a hole it did go,
And over its shoulder poor Mary did throw.

They carried her home—she recovered next day;
But her ass it was left in the hole where it lay.
Its poor neck was broken—Och! bless me soul!
And the people all round call it Mary's Ass Hole.
And Mary regretted the loss of her ass,
And oft of an evening by there she would pass,
And lately I've noticed as by there I stroll
There's some very bad smells come from Mary's Ass Hole.

Several elderly people have told John Meredith that Henry Lawson wrote 'The Dogs' Meeting' as well as the well-known 'Shearer's Lament'. When John was taking part in a concert at Mudgee, some time ago, an old man told him that he was with Lawson when he wrote it. They were sitting, the old chap said, on a seat outside one of the local pubs watching the dogs do what dogs do when they meet, and afterwards, in the bar, Henry wrote out the ballad and read it aloud. There are certainly a lot of dogs about Mudgee streets even today and Lawson certainly knew his dogs (see, for example, 'The Shearing of the Cook's Dog', 'That There Dog of Mine', 'The Loaded Dog', or 'Two Dogs and a Fence'), but whether he actually wrote these verses has been doubted by several reputable authorities.

When Bill Boundy sang 'The Dogs' Meeting' he thumped on a table with a *boom, boom-boom* rhythm in place of some words. A popular song of a few years ago, sung to the same tune, used the same method of replacing words with a *thump, thump-thump.*

THE DOGS' MEETING

Oh, the dogs once held a concert,
They came from near and far,
Oh, some they came by aeroplane,
And some by motor car.
Before into the concert hall
They were allowed to look,
Each dog had to take his (boom, boom-boom)
And hang it on a hook.
Oh, each dog had to take his (boom, boom-boom)
And hang it on a hook.

Oh, hardly were they seated there,
Each mother, son and sire,
When a dirty little yeller dog
Began to holler 'Fire!'
Out they rushed in panic—
They didn't stop to look—
Each dog he grabbed a (boom, boom-boom)
From off the nearest hook.

Bill Coughlin singing 'The Union Boy' (possibly with his mind on the glasses of stout to follow)

Above: Herb Gimbert, self-taught musician, playing the tin whistle

Left: Tom Gibbons of Gulgong in the yard of the Centennial Hotel, which was owned by his son.
This is typical of his stance while singing

Below: Jack Luscombe, who had a great fund of reminiscences as well as songs, with two of his wife's ancestors

Above: Mick Pilley, the Mudgee fiddler. Mick was taught to play by his father, who learned from an Irish immigrant

Below: Fred Large and Arthur Davis in the yard of the house at Ulan that was so readily lent for recording purposes

Sally Sloane

Above: Sally Sloane with a portrait of her mother and stepfather.
Many songs and tunes from her Irish grandmother came
to Sally via her mother

Below: Cyril Abbott with the kerosene-tin dulcimer. This is an
experimental model, and the hole under the strings is not usual

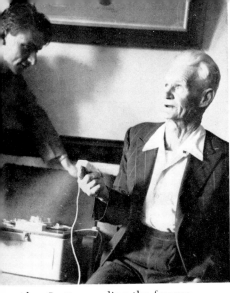

Alan Scott recording the famous 'Duke' Tritton

Many a bush sing-song took place at Cyril Abbott's home at Mudgee. *Left to right*: Arthur Davis, Les Davis, Cyril Abbott and John Meredith

Frank Adams of Windeyer, near Mudgee. Frank lost his left hand in a chaffcutter at the age of 16; undaunted, he restrung his fiddle back to front and learned to play that way

Fred Holland, of Mudgee, swinging the concertina to get that peculiar ringing tone so liked by the old hands

Fred Holland with three of his five musical sons.
From left: Vince, Fred, Neville and Merv

Joe Cashmere with the fiddle he played for over sixty years

And that's the reason why you see,
On walking down the street,
Each dog will stop and swap a smell
With every dog he meets.
And that's the reason why a dog
Will leave a good fat bone
To go and smell a (boom, boom-boom)
In hope to find his own.
To go and smell a (boom, boom-boom)
In hope to find his own.

'The Dogs' Meeting' was recorded at Fred Sloane's house in Lithgow. When Boundy had completed his song, Fred remarked that he had never heard it sung before, only as a recitation, so Meredith recorded him as well.

On the same day Fred told Meredith of the toast used to conclude the funeral service for a very dead leg of mutton served on a Dardanelles-bound troopship.

TOAST
The Lord of Love look from above
Upon this leg of mutton:
Once 'twas sweet and fit to eat,
But now, by God, it's rotten!

Sally Sloane

Sally Sloane was born at Parkes in 1894. Her grandmother, Sarah Alexander, came from County Kerry, Ireland, by sailing ship in 1838 when she was aged twenty-two years. According to family tradition, she was a trained singer. Convicts were building Circular Quay when she and her brother arrived in Sydney.

Sarah married Dick Burrowes, and, after he died, Charles Dean. She died in 1888 at the age of seventy-two years. Her first daughter was also named Sarah, and she when she grew up learned to play concertina, button accordion, jew's-harp, and piano. She also was a good singer and learned many of the old Irish songs from her mother. She married Tom Frost, who, along with his father, Jim Frost, was a driver for Cobb and Co. Later Sarah divorced him and married William Clegg, a goldminer who afterwards worked in many parts of New South Wales as a railway construction worker.

L

Sarah Frost's first daughter was also named Sarah, but called Sally by common usage. She inherited the family gift of singing and learning songs easily. All her mother's instruments plus the fiddle, mouthorgan and tin whistle were mastered by her.

Sally and her husband, Fred Sloane, were living at Lithgow when John Meredith first met them, but later moved to Teralba, on the shore of Lake Macquarie. Unfortunately none of Sally Sloane's children have inherited her love of folk song and it was a stroke of luck that Meredith was able to record her extensive repertoire. He contacted the Sloanes in 1954 and had regular two-monthly recording sessions until 1961. Sally kept remembering further items; in fact, there seemed no end to the songs and tunes she knew. The bulk of these were learned from her mother, but several came from her step-father, William Clegg, and other bush workers.

Sally Sloane would often burst into song while washing the dishes, but by the time she had finished her task the song or tune would be forgotten. After losing a few items this way, John Meredith thought up the idea of hanging the microphone over the sink and switching on the recorder whenever Sally began to sing. Later, a second recording, free from the clatter of dishes, was made of anything worth while. Mrs Sloane told Meredith that, as children, she and her sister always sang the old songs while washing and wiping the dinner dishes—probably that is why they float into consciousness immediately she takes up the dishmop.

THE RED ROSE TOP

I'll cut off the red rose top,
And plant the willow green, green.
In all this world that you may see,
It's slighted I have been, been,
It's slighted I have been.

Oh, when your thyme is pulled and gone,
They care no more for you, you.
There's not a place your thyme goes waste,
But it spreads all over with rue, rue,
It spreads all over with rue.

'The Red Rose Top' was one of Sally Sloane's grandmother's
songs; she also called it 'The Sprig of Thyme'. Actually, both
come from a very old English song, generally known as 'The
Seeds of Love', which has a meaning quite easily interpreted as
a symbol of virginity by those familiar with the 'language of the
flowers'.

Two versions in E. K. Wells's *The Ballad Tree*, one titled 'The
Seeds of Love' and the other 'Keep Your Garden Clean', were
originally two distinct songs which appear to have borrowed
from each other. Each contains lines similar to lines in Sally
Sloane's version, but her tune may be much older, as it is
markedly different.

Broadwood and Fuller Maitland print three tunes and two
sets of words, all very different from the Sloane version. Other
versions by various names appeared in Kidson's *Traditional
Tunes*, Baring Gould's *Songs and Ballads of the West*, and Bell's
Ancient Poems, Ballads and Songs of the Peasantry. Baring
Gould's notes state: 'Taken down from James Parsons. After the
second verse he broke away to "I sowed the seeds of love", a
well-known folk-song composed about 1670 by Mrs Fleetwood
Habergram to the air of "Come open the door, sweet Betty",
and to that melody it is usually sung.'

Sally Sloane sang a beautiful modal version of 'Ben Hall', one
that was learned from her mother. The same song was sung by
the late Bruce Crocket of Dripstone, New South Wales. Crocket
was a friend of Sally's mother and played his concertina at her
wedding to Tom Frost. Whether she learned the ballad from
Crocket, he from her, or both from another source, is not known.

BEN HALL

Come, all you young Australians, and everyone besides,
I'll sing to you a ditty that will fill you with surprise,
Concerning of a 'ranger bold, whose name it was Ben Hall,
But cruelly murdered was this day, which proved his downfall.

An outcast from society, he was forced to take the road,
All through his false and treacherous wife, who sold off his abode.
He was hunted like a native dog from bush to hill and dale,
Till he turned upon his enemies and they could not find his trail.

All out with his companions, men's blood he scorned to shed,
He oft-times stayed their lifted hands, with vengeance on their heads.
No petty, mean or pilfering act he ever stooped to do,
But robbed the rich and hearty man, and scorned to rob the poor.

One night as he in ambush lay all on the Lachlan Plain,
When, thinking everything secure, to ease himself had lain,
When to his consternation and to his great surprise,
And without one moment's warning, a bullet past him flies.

And it was soon succeeded by a volley sharp and loud,
With twelve revolving rifles all pointed at his head.
'Where are you, Gilbert? Where is Dunn?' he loudly did call.
It was all in vain, they were not there to witness his downfall.

They riddled all his body as if they were afraid,
But in his dying moment he breathed curses on their heads.

164

That cowardly hearted Condel, the sergeant of the police,
He crept and fired with fiendish glee till death did him release.

Although he had a lion's heart, more braver than the brave,
Those cowards shot him like a dog—no word of challenge gave.
Though many friends had poor Ben Hall, his enemies were few,
Like the emblems of his native land, his days were numbered too.

It's through Australia's sunny clime Ben Hall will roam no more.
His name is spread both near and far to every distant shore.
For generations after this parents will to their children call,
And rehearse to them the daring deeds committed by Ben Hall.

Her mother often told Sally tales of Ben Hall, some of which she, in turn, recorded for John Meredith.

'Mother knew Ben Hall's sister-in-law,' Sally said. 'Yes, she brought me into the world.

'I saw the place where Ben Hall was killed. He lay down to have a rest this day and was ambushed. Yes, it was near Forbes, on the Lachlan Plain—he lay down to have a rest, and Coobung Mick always used to look after his money for him. He lay there this day waiting for Coobung Mick to bring food to him. Instead of bringing food he brought the cops. And when the policemen come, they surrounded him and riddled his body with bullets, and Mrs Coobung Mick knew that her husband used to look after the money for Ben Hall and when she heard all these here shots going into poor Ben Hall she put her fingers to her ears and said, "Oh, my God! Poor Ben! That's Ben," she said. "My husband has betrayed him."

'And she was carrying a child at the time (said by some to be Ben Hall's) and when the child was born it had thirty-two spots on it, and that child was exhibited through the length and breadth of Australia for show purposes [as the Leopard Boy]. The spots were supposed to correspond with the thirty-two bullet wounds in Hall's body!'

Mrs Sloane continued, 'Poor Ben Hall, he had a property of his own, near Forbes, and all the bad deeds that used to be done were pinned onto poor Ben Hall. And he was yarding his cattle this day and they come onto him and took him into Forbes for trial for something that he didn't do, and all his cattle were left in the yard. Instead of the police pulling the sliprails down and letting them out, they was all left to perish.

'And when he come out after doing a month in jail they were just carcasses in the yard. They burned his place down. His wife had betrayed him and went off with another man. And the black-feller, he took to the bush, he and his gin.

'Ben took to the bush then, and turned out to be a highway-man. When he found out what had happened, his wife had gone, and his stock and everything was destroyed and he become a bushranger.'

THE BANKS OF CLAUDY

It was on a summer's morning all in the month of May,
Down by the banks of Claudy I carelessly did stray.
I overheard a female in sorrow to complain,
All for her absent lover that ploughed the raging main.

I stepped up unto her and gave her a big surprise;
I hoped she did not know me, I be in such disguise.
I says, 'My fairest creature, my joy and heart's delight,
How far do you mean to wander this dark and dreary night?'

'It's to the banks of Claudy, if you'll be pleased to show,
Take pity on a fair maid, who knows not where to go.
I'm searching for a young man, and Johnnie is his name,
And on the banks of Claudy I'm told he does remain.'

'These are the banks of Claudy, fair maid, whereon you stand,
But do not trust your Johnnie, for he's a false young man.
But do not trust your Johnnie, for he'll not meet you here,
But tarry with me in green woods, no danger need you fear.'

'If Johnnie was here this night he would keep me from all harm,
He's in the field of battle, all in his uniform,
He's in the field of battle and his foes he does defy,
Like the loyal king of honour all on the walls of Troy.'

'It's six long weeks or better since Johnnie left this shore,
A-crossing the main ocean where thundering billows roar,
A-crossing the main ocean for honour and for fame,
But I'm told the ship was wrecked nigh to the coast of Spain.'

And when she heard this dreadful news, she flew in deep despair,
A-wringing of her hands and a-tearing of her hair,
Saying, 'If my Johnnie's drowned, no man alive I'll take;
Through lonesome shades and valleys I'll wander, all for his sake.'

When he saw her loyalty, no longer could he stand,
He flew into her arms, saying, 'Betsy, I'm the man!'
Saying, 'Betsy, I'm the young man, the cause of all your pain,
Now since we've met on Claudy banks, we'll never part again.'

This fine English folk song came to Sally Sloane through her
mother. Several versions have been published, notably those in
Kidson's *Traditional Tunes* and the *Journal of the Folk Song
Society* (nos. 1 and 13). Colm O Lochlainn gives an Irish song
with similar words, but set to a totally different tune.

Sally Sloane's grandmother first taught 'The Maid of Fainey'
to her daughter, who in turn passed it on to Sally.

THE MAID OF FAINEY

There was a maid of Fainey, of youth and beauty bright,
Who had scores of sweethearts to court her day and night.
But she had one only true love and he was her father's man,
And if I am not mistaken I think his name was John.

167

For they both walked out together all in her father's park,
For they both sat down together to have some private talk,
Saying, 'Here is a token of true love,' and the ring he broke in two,
Saying, 'You keep one-half, my love, and I'll do the same for you.'

Just as the ring was broken, she was in his arms entwined,
Whilst her poor aged father stood all the while behind,
Saying, 'Daughter, if I catch him, some refreshments he will have,
I will send him to some far off land, where he'll be treated as a slave.'

'Oh, father, I'll go with him, let hard not be your heart—
If he draws a cart like horses, with him I'll draw my cart.'
'Oh, daughter, I'll confine you all in your silent room;
I'll give you bread and water, and that will be your doom.'

'I don't want your bread and water, nor anything you have,
If you rob me of my Johnnie, I'll go down to the silent grave.'
Not another word was spoken, not so much as 'Fare-thee-well',
For her heart-strings they were broken, which rang the parting knell.

'The Wee One' is a warning to 'young men that is fond of the lassies' with a difference; usually 'the woman pays'—according to women. The song was learned from Bob Vaughan, of Aberdeen, New South Wales.

THE WEE ONE

I am a young man cut down in my blossom,
I married a young girl to comfort my home.
She goes out and she leaves me
And falsely deceives me
And leaves me a wee one that ne'er was my own.
Oh, dear, oh, the day I got married,
I wish I were single again,
With my weeping and wailing
And rocking the cradle
And nursing a wee one that ne'er is my own.

While I'm at work, my wife's on the rantan,
On the rantan with another young man.
She goes out and she leaves me
And falsely deceives me
And leaves me a wee one that ne'er is my own.
Oh, dear, oh, etc.

All you young men that is fond of the lassies
Take my advice, leave those flash girls alone,
For by the Lord Harry
If one you should marry,
They'll bring you a wee one that ne'er is your own.
Oh, dear, oh, etc.

'The Cherry Tree' was another of the songs that came to Sally
Sloane from her grandmother, via her mother.

THE CHERRY TREE

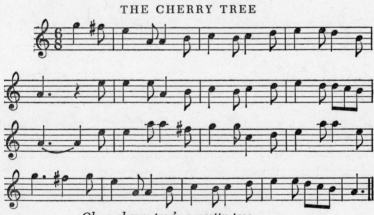

Oh, a cherry tree's a pretty tree
When it is in full bloom;
And so is a handsome young man
When he a-courting goes.

With not a penny in his purse,
He'll curse, and swear it's full,
And not a home or anything
To bring a fair maid to.

Oh, I long for to get married
And so did all my life.
I long for to get married,
So I'll go choose a wife.
[Half verse forgotten]

Oh, now he has got married and
He's brought her home to sorrow;
The land it is to purchase,
The money it is to borrow.
She can sit down in the corner,
And she can cry her fill,
For she drank the ale that she loved best,
She took him with good will.

Sally Sloane learned 'If I Was a Blackbird' from an old Irishman, Peter Owens, who sang and played the flute. She boarded with his daughter for some time and occasionally accompanied the old chap on her fiddle. In *Irish Street Ballads* there is a song (no. 46) the tune of which differs slightly from Sally Sloane's version.

IF I WAS A BLACKBIRD

If I was a blackbird I'd whistle and sing,
And I'd follow the ship that my true love sailed in,
And on the top rigging I'd there build my nest,
And pillow my head in his lily-white breast.

170

I am a young maiden and my story is sad,
For once I was courted by a brave sailor lad.
He courted me strongly by day and by night,
But now my dear sailor has gone far away.

He promised to take me to Donnybrook fair
To buy me red ribbons to bind up my hair,
And when he'd return from the ocean so wide
He'd take me and make me his own loving bride.

His parents they slighted me and will not agree
That I and my sailor boy married should be,
But when he comes home I will greet him with joy,
And I'll take to my bosom my dear sailor boy.

'The Girls of the Shamrock Shore', as sung by Sally Sloane, is a fragment of a song known to her grandmother, and is included here for its local reference and the rather lovely tune which, in variant forms, is used for a number of Irish songs. O Lochlainn prints 'A New Song Called Granuaile', a variant of this song.

THE GIRLS OF THE SHAMROCK SHORE

It being in the spring
When the small birds sing
And the lambs do sport and play,
I entered as a passenger,
To New South Wales sailed o'er;
And I'll bid farewell
To all that dwell,
And the girls of the shamrock shore.

A fragment of another old Irish ballad that Sally Sloane's grandmother used to sing is 'Lovely Molly', also included in this book for its tune.

LOVELY MOLLY

Oh, meeting is a pleasure
Between my love and I;
I'll go down to yon green valley
To meet my love by and by.
I'll go down to yon green valley
To meet my heart's delight.
Oh, pity me, lovely Molly,
This dark and rainy night.

I bought my love a bottle
And placed it in her hand,
Saying, 'Fill and drink, lovely Molly,
Our courtship's at a stand.
[Rest of song missing]

'The Green Bushes' is well known in England and appears in most major collections of English folk song. Broadwood and Fuller Maitland's *English County Songs* gives a tune in the major key for words very much the same as Sally Sloane's, which she sings to a modal tune. The Rev. S. Baring Gould, who supplied Broadwood and Fuller Maitland with both tune and words,

172

prints a different air in his *Songs and Ballads of the West*. Kidson, again, has a minor air for the song in his *Traditional Tunes*, and Joyce's *Ancient Irish Music* gives three variants, major and and minor, for the same song.

Sally Sloane learned her version from an English railway construction worker, Jack Archer, when she was twelve years of age. We give the verses of the song in the order that she sang them, but stanza 4 may well be the penultimate one.

THE GREEN BUSHES

As I went a-walking one morning in spring,
To hear the birds whistle and the nightingale sing,
I spied a fair damsel, so sweetly sang she,
Down by the green bushes where she thinks to meet me.

'Oh, what are you loitering for, my pretty maid?'
'I'm a-loitering for my true love, kind sir,' she said.
'Shall I be your true love, and will you agree
To forsake your own true love and go along with me?'

'Oh, come, let us be going, kind sir, if you please,
Come, let us be going from under those trees.
Oh, yonder is coming my true love, I see,
Down by the green bushes where he thinks to meet me.'

Oh, when he came there and found she was gone
He looked all around him and cried quite forlorn,
Saying, 'She's gone with some other and quite forsaken me,
So adieu to those green bushes for ever!' cried he.

173

'I'll buy you fine beaver, and fine silken gowns,
I'll buy you fine petticoats flounced to the ground.
If you'll prove loyal and constant [will] be,
And forsake your own true love and go along with me.'

'I want none of your petticoats nor your fine silken robes:
I was never so foolish as to marry for clothes.
But if you'll prove loyal and constant and true
I'll forsake my own true love and go along with you.'

'I'll be like some schoolboy, I'll spend all my time in play,
For I never was so foolish as to be lured away.
No false-hearted young girl shall serve me so any more,
So adieu to those green bushes, it's time to give o'er.'

Jack Archer was also the source from whom Sally Sloane learned 'The Rambling Sailor'. Cecil Sharp prints English versions in *Folk Songs from Somerset*, series 4, and *English Folk Songs*, Selected Edition, vol. 1, while the *Journal of the Folk Song Society*, nos. 11 and 18, also prints versions collected in England.

THE RAMBLING SAILOR

(Mixolydian Mode)

I am a sailor stout and bold,
Long years I've ploughed the ocean,
To fight for my king and country, too,
For honour and promotion.
I said, 'Brother sailors, I'll bid you all adieu;
I'll go no more to sea with you.
I'll travel the country through and through
And I'll still be a rambling sailor.'

Oh, when I came to Greenwich town,
Of lassies there were plenty,
So boldly I stepped up to one
To court her for her beauty.
I said, 'My dear, what do you choose,
There's brandy, ale and rum punch, too,
Besides a pair of new silk shoes
To travel with your rambling sailor?

'Oh, if you wish to know my name,
My name it is young Johnson,
I have a commission from the king
To court all girls at Sanson.
With my false heart and flattering tongue,
I'll court them all both old and young,
I'll court them all and marry none,
And I'll still be a rambling sailor.'

Oh, when I woke up in the morn
I left my dear a-sleeping,
I left her for an hour or two,
While I go court some other.
With my false heart and flattering tongue,
I'll court them all both old and young,
I'll court them all but marry none,
And I'll still be a rambling sailor.

[4 lines missing]
Oh, they put me to lay on the cold barn floor,
And the wind and the rain blew between two doors,
'You can put him in bed with me, mother,
For they tell me he's a rambling sailor.'

As noted earlier, the tune of 'The Girl with the Flowing Hair' as sung by Sally Sloane is very similar to that used by Ben Castle for 'Moriarity'. Sally learned the song, a fragment only remaining today, from Billy Page, an old goldminer at Parkes.

THE GIRL WITH THE FLOWING HAIR

My heart went pitty pitty patty
As she passed me by so beautiful and fair.
Oh, she winked at me with her soft blue eye,
The girl with the flowing hair.

A second song learned in Parkes, this time from Harry Bartlett, a goldminer who worked with Sally's father when she was a girl, has no connection with the well-known 'Wild Rover No More'. John Meredith has recorded fragments of 'I've Been a Wild Boy' from other singers, including Leo Dixon.

I'VE BEEN A WILD BOY

Oh, my father he died and he left me his estate,
I married a lady whose fortune was great,
And through keeping bad company I've spent all my store.
I have been a wild boy, but I'll be so no more.

Oh, there was Bill, Tom and Harry and Betsy and Sue
And two or three others belonged to our crew;
We sat up till midnight and made the town roar.
Oh, I've been a wild boy, but I'll be so no more.

I was always too fond of treating ladies to wine,
Till my pockets grew empty too soon I would find;
Twenty pounds in one night, oh, I've spent them and more.
Oh, I've been a wild boy, but I'll be so no more.

Oh, it's first down to Newgate a prisoner I went;
I had on cold irons, I had to lament,
And I had to find comfort as I lay on the floor.
Oh, I've been a wild boy, but I'll be so no more.

Oh, the next down to Newgate, a prisoner I stand,
And what I have longed for is now out of hand;
And if ever I gain my liberty as I've had before,
I will be a good boy, as I have been before.

Oh, bad luck to all married men who visit strange doors,
I've done so myself, but I'll do so no more;
I'll go home to my family, I'll go home to my wife,
And I'll be a good boy all the rest of my life.

Songs of Scotland, edited by Myles Foster, contains Robert
Burns's version of 'Lady Mary Ann', which tells the same story
as Sally Sloane's song, 'My Bonny Love Is Young'.

MY BONNY LOVE IS YOUNG

Oh Mother, oh Mother, you done a thing what's wrong,
You married me to a college boy, whose age is far too young,
For my age is twice ten, and my love he is sixteen,
And my bonny boy is young and he's growing.

Dear daughter, dear daughter, I'll tell you what I'll do,
I'll send him off to college for another year or two,
And on his Scotch cap I will tie a bunch of blue,
For to let the ladies know that he's married,
For to let the ladies know that he's married.

'Lovely Nancy' was passed on to Sally Sloane from Sarah
Alexander, who sang it many times at concerts during the voyage
to Australia.

M

Adieu, my lovely Nancy,
Ten thousand times adieu;
I'm going to cross the ocean
To seek for something new.
Come, change your ring with me, my dear,
Come, change your ring with me,
It will be a token of true love,
When I am on the sea.

When I am on the sea, my love,
And you know not where I am,
But letters I will write to you
From every foreign land
With the secrets of my mind, my dear,
And the best of my good will.
And let my body be where it will,
My heart will be with you still.

See how the storm is rising,
See how it's coming on,
While we poor jolly jack tars
Are fighting for the Crown.
Our captain he commands us,
And his orders we must obey,
Expecting every moment
For to be cast away.

Now the storm is over,
And we are safe on shore,
We will drink to our wives and sweethearts
And the girls we do adore.
We'll call for liquor merrily,
And spend our money free,
And when our money it's all gone,
We'll boldly go to sea.

'The Lowlands of Holland' is a famous and often-printed folk song. In *The Singing Englishman* (p. 16) A. L. Lloyd has a song with almost identical words called 'The Spermwhale Fishery', concerned with the grief of a Lincolnshire bride whose newly-wed husband was shanghaied and taken to the Arctic whaling grounds. The tune given by Lloyd is entirely different. Another version differing from Sally Sloane's but containing in two of the three verses the lines

> *'the lowlands o' Holland*
> *Hae twinn'd my love and me'*

appeared in Pittman, Brown, and Mackey's *Songs of Scotland*.

THE LOWLANDS OF HOLLAND

When I was first married, laid up in marriage bed,
There came a bold sea captain, and stood at my bed-head.
Saying, 'Rise, arise, you married man, and come along with me,
To the lowlands of Holland, that lies between my love and me.'

[3 lines missing]
For the lowlands of Holland that has parted my love and me.

John Meredith gathered several versions of 'The Coolgardie Miner', sometimes called 'Castles in the Air', from Australian singers. Sally Sloane's mother learned the following version in the Parkes area.

THE COOLGARDIE MINER

The scene was at Coolgardie,
And in a tent one night

180

Sat an English miner
Beneath the pale moonlight.
A thousand thoughts in memory
Came before him to unfold
As he pictured dear old England,
The land he'd left for gold.

CHORUS:

> *He thought of his home, sweet home,*
> *Across all the restless foam,*
> *He thought of his father and mother so dear,*
> *Waiting some news from their boy to hear;*
> *His sweetheart, he'd vowed to be true*
> *Until their wedding day.*
> *How he longed, yes, he longed for the absent ones*
> *And the dear old home far away.*

As he sat and gazed on a photo
Of a group of friends at home,
And as he gazed upon it
The tears they somehow come.
He thought of his dear old mother,
His father growing old,
And he pictured dear old England,
The land he left for gold.

It's just one year ago today
Since he sailed across the foam,
To earn some mortgage money
That was owed his childhood home.
Thank God, his luck has changed at last
And before a week is o'er
He'll sail back to old England,
To leave it nevermore.

A varsovienna played on the button accordion by Sally is the same as that played by Mick Pilley of Mudgee. As Mrs Sloane knew Mick's sister in her younger days at Home Rule, John Meredith thought this was the probable source, but Sally says she learned the tune from Bob Vaughan of Aberdeen. The second part of the melody is similar to that played by Joe Cashmere.

Bob Vaughan taught Mrs Sloane some half a dozen jigs and hornpipes. Among them was 'Coming Down the Mountain', which she plays on the fiddle.

COMING DOWN THE MOUNTAIN

One of the many dance tunes known to Sally Sloane had no proper name and when one of the family wanted her to play it they simply requested her to 'play Jack's waltz, Sal'. In time it became known in the Sloane household as 'Jack's Waltz'. John Mountford of Molong taught it to Sally.

JACK'S WALTZ

Another pretty waltz tune played on the accordion by Sally Sloane received its name in the same way. Annie Shaw was the name of a young girl who lived next door to the Frost family at Parkes. Each Friday evening during the visit to the house by her sweetheart, Annie Shaw accompanied her young man's violin playing on the piano. They regularly performed the waltz tune together, and Sally Sloane had no difficulty in learning it as the music floated over the side fence. The family always referred to the tune as 'Annie Shaw's Tune'.

The final example of Sally Sloane's amazing repertoire of dance tunes is entitled 'Mum's Mazurka'.

This was one of the tunes Sally learned from her mother, who was, as mentioned earlier, a competent bush musician on the concertina, accordion, piano, and jew's-harp. Played with emphasized rhythm, the tune has a wonderful swinging 'lift' to it.

As danced in the bush, the mazurka—or polka-mazurka, as it was sometimes called—resembled the varsovienna in both step and form.

184

'A New Song on the Manchester Martyrs' or 'The Smashing of the Van' in *Irish Street Ballads* uses the same tune as Sally Sloane's song of the wild colonial boy, 'John Doolan'. What is usually a chorus is treated as verse 2 in this song.

JOHN DOOLAN

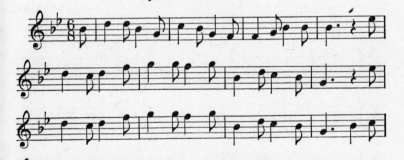

It's of a wild colonial boy, John Doolan was his name,
Of poor but honest parents he was born in Castlemaine.
He was his father's only hope, his mother's only joy,
And so dearly did the parents love their wild colonial boy.

Then come along, my hearties, and we'll roam the mountains high,
Together we will plunder, together we will die.
We'll wander o'er the valleys and we'll gallop over plains,
And we'll scorn to live in slavery bound down in iron chains.

'Twas in eighteen hundred and sixty-five he started his wild career,
With a heart that had no danger, no foeman did he fear.
He stuck up the Royal Mail beach coach and robbed Judge MacEvoy;
With a tremble hand gave up the gold to the wild colonial boy.

As John rode out one morning, and riding slowly on,
When listening to the little birds, they sweetly sang their song,
He spied three mounted troopers—Kelly, Davis and Fitzroy—
All riding up to capture the wild colonial boy.

'Surrender now, Jack Doolan! You see there's three to one.
Surrender in the Queen's name! It's of a victory won.'
He fired at trooper Kelly and he brought him to the ground,
And returning right to Davis he received a mortal wound.

The accompanying fragment of 'The Wallaby Track', sung to a variant of 'Donald of Glencoe', is not from E. J. Overbury's poem, 'On the Wallaby Track'. Sally Sloane learned the song from a girl named Jo Bowen of Tambar Springs in the north-west of New South Wales.

THE WALLABY TRACK

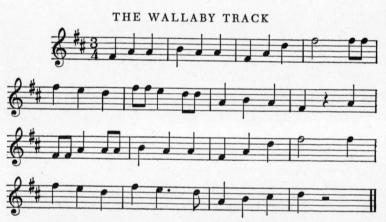

Roll up your bundle and make a neat swag,
Collar onto your billycan and the old tuckerbag.
It's no disgrace to be seen with your swag on your back,
While searching for work on the wallaby track.

'The Springtime It Brings On the Shearing' was printed in Overbury's *Bush Poems*, published by the Creswick and Clunes *Advertiser* in 1865. It comes from the longer poem just mentioned, 'On the Wallaby Track'. Seemingly only a few stanzas passed into the oral tradition and acquired a tune.

THE SPRINGTIME IT BRINGS ON THE SHEARING

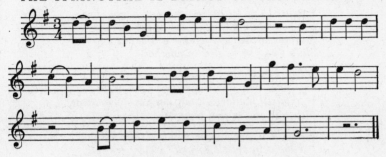

You have heard of those flash country shearers,
The flashest in all the town,
But there is none that is flash as the shearer,
A shearer when shearing comes round.

Now that the wool season's over,
And the shearing is now at an end,
It's now you will see those flash shearers
Cooking johnny-cakes down in the bend.

In *Songs and Ballads of the West* Baring Gould included a song entitled 'The False Bride', which is a textual variant of Sally Sloane's 'I Think by This Time He's Forgot Her', sung to a totally different tune. Baring Gould mentions two more versions in his notes.

I THINK BY THIS TIME HE'S FORGOT HER

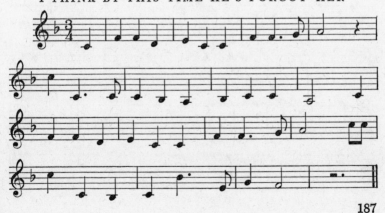

187

The week before Easter, the place of Dunclare,
Bright shines the sun, but a very cold air,
I went to the forest, some posies to pull,
But the forest it yield me no posies.

I courted this fair maid for many a long day.
See how she's rewarded me at the last day;
See how she's rewarded me at the last day—
She's going to be tied to another.

When breakfast was ready no meat could I eat,
I preferred my love's company far before meat;
I preferred my love's company far before meat,
Although she is tied to another.

When breakfast was over to bed they did go,
I thought to myself I should lay by her side;
I thought to myself I should lie by her side,
Although she is tied to another.

Oh, dig me a grave, dig it wide, long and deep,
And plant it all over with flowers so sweet,
And lay me down there till I have a long sleep,
And I think by that time I'll forget her.

They dug him a grave, dug it large, wide and deep,
And planted all over with flowers so sweet,
And laid him down there till he had a long sleep,
I think by this time he's forgot her.

Yet another song of Sally Sloane's grandmother passed down through her mother is 'The Journeyman Tailor'.

THE JOURNEYMAN TAILOR

As I went a-walking one bright summer's day,
When a young journeyman tailor was going my way.
He was brisk and airy, she saw him pass by,
She called to this young man and bid him draw nigh.

'Where are you going, and what is your name?
Where was you born, please tell me the same?'
'I was born near Derry, fair lady,' said he,
And James is the name that my godfather gave me.'

'Oh, James, I would have you to wed, love, with me,
And you shall have your footman to wait upon thee;
You shall have your footman when you go to ride,
And when you be wed, love, I will be your fond bride.'

'Fair lady, your speeches does please me well now,
But our birth and education would never agree;
Our birth and education would never agree,
And some countryman's daughter is more suited for me.'

Religious folk songs—or traditional carols—are extremely rare in Australia. 'Christ Was Born in Bethlehem' is the only example of this kind recorded by John Meredith. Other versions have appeared in print in the United States of America, first in Botsford's *Folk Songs of Many Peoples*, where it is simply noted as a 'Kentucky song', and more recently in E. K. Wells's book, *The Ballad Tree*. Miss Wells collected her version in the Kentucky mountains and includes the lines sung by Sally Sloane in a slightly different form to a somewhat different tune.

CHRIST WAS BORN IN BETHLEHEM

189

Christ was born in Bethlehem,
Christ was born in Bethlehem,
Christ was born in Bethlehem
And in a manger lay.
And in a manger lay,
And in a manger lay,
Christ was born in Bethlehem
And in a manger lay.

The Jews they crucified him,
The Jews they crucified him,
The Jews they crucified him
And nailed him to a tree.
And nailed him to a tree,
And nailed him to a tree,
The Jews they crucified him
And nailed him to a tree.

Mary she came weeping,
Mary she came weeping,
Mary she came weeping
And stole away my Lord.
And stole away my Lord,
And stole away my Lord,
Mary she came weeping
And stole away my Lord.

Arthur Davis (p. 223) recites a complete text of 'The Warrego Lament', often known as 'She's the Tart for a Bushman';
Sally Sloane sings one verse.

THE WARREGO LAMENT

She's the tart for a bushman,
She'll drink rum and she'll smoke,
In her hand she carries a boomerang,
She wears the possum cloak.
I will wash your greasy pants
While shearing in the shine,
If you'll take me back again, old boy,
To that old gal of mine.

Owing to its appearance in school readers for many years, Henry Lawson's 'Ballad of the Drover' is probably his most generally known work in verse. Sally Sloane has been singing the ballad to one of her mother's Irish tunes since she was a girl.

BALLAD OF THE DROVER

Across the stony ridges, across the rolling plain,
Young Harry Dale, the drover, comes riding home again.
And well his stock-horse bears him, and light of heart is he,
And stoutly his old packhorse is trotting by his knee.

Up Queensland way with cattle he's travelled regions vast,
And many months have vanished since home-folks saw him last.
He hums a song of someone he hopes to marry soon,
And hobble-chains and camp-ware keep jingling to the tune.

Beyond the hazy dado against the lower skies
And yon blue line of ranges the station homestead lies.
And thitherward the drover jogs through the lazy noon,
While hobble-chains and camp-ware are jingling to a tune.

An hour has filled the heavens with storm-clouds inky black;
At times the lightning trickles around the drover's track;
But Harry pushes onward, his horses' strength he tries,
In hope to reach the river before the flood shall rise.

The thunder, pealing o'er him, goes rumbling down the plain;
And sweet on thirsty pastures beats fast the plashing rain;
Then every creek and gully sends forth its tribute flood—
The river runs a banker, all stained with yellow mud.

Now Harry speaks to Rover, the best dog on the plains,
And to his hardy horses, and strokes their shaggy manes:
'We've breasted bigger rivers when floods were at their height,
Nor shall this gutter stop us from getting home tonight!'

The thunder growls a warning, the blue, forked lightnings gleam;
The drover turns his horses to swim the fatal stream.
But, oh! the flood runs stronger than e'er it ran before;
The saddle-horse is failing, and only half-way o'er!

When flashes next the lightning, the flood's grey breast is blank;
A cattle-dog and packhorse are struggling up the bank.
But in the lonely homestead the girl shall wait in vain—
He'll never pass the stations in charge of stock again.

The faithful dog a moment lies panting on the bank,
Then plunges through the current to where his master sank.
And round and round in circles he fights with failing strength,
Till, gripped by wider waters, he fails and sinks at length.

Across the flooded lowlands and slopes of sodden loam
The packhorse struggles bravely to take dumb tidings home;
And mud-stained, wet, and weary, he goes by rock and tree,
With clanging chains and tinware all sounding eerily.

Unfortunately, a number of Mrs Sloane's songs are only fragments as far as words are concerned, but the tunes are complete in every instance. Two examples follow. The first, 'The
Black Velvet Band', came to Sally Sloane from Billy Page, the
Parkes goldminer.

THE BLACK VELVET BAND

The judge he passed sentence next morning,
And a free trip to Van Diemen's Land—
Far, far from my friends and relations
And the girl with the black velvet band.

The fragment of 'The Shoemaker's Son' came to Sally Sloane from her grandmother.

THE SHOEMAKER'S SON

Young Jimmy was a shoemaker's son,
And through this country his bread he won.
Her father was of high degree,
He was captain over some ships on sea.

Sally Sloane's 'Click Go the Shears' is a variant fragment of songs of the same name, and was learned by her from her step-father, William Clegg.

CLICK GO THE SHEARS

193

Now, Mister Newchum, for to begin,
In number seven paddock bring all the sheep in;
Don't leave none behind, whatever you may do,
And then you'll be fit for a jackeroo.

CHORUS:

    Click go the shears, click, click, click,
    Wide are the blows and his hand moves quick.
    The ringer looks around, sees he's beaten by a blow,
    And he curses that old shearer with that bare-bellied yoe.

Her mother taught Sally a song she called 'Gargal Machree', which appears to be a corruption of 'Grá Geal Mo Chroí', but the Irish ballads of the same name are entirely different in text and tune to this.

GARGAL MACHREE

    Oh, straight to her father has he, underhand,
    And he gave him a letter, as I understand,
    And as soon as he read it he swore bitterly
    That he'd alter the case with my Gargal Machree.

    He called for his daughter with scorn and disdain,
    Saying, 'Here's a letter from your darling swain.'
    And as soon as he read it he swore bitterly
    That he'd alter the case with my Gargal Machree.

    It's then, this fair maiden she fell on her knees,
    Saying, 'Honoured father, then do as you please,
    But if ever I should lose him, it's torn I should be;
    I'll never disown, I'm his Gargal Machree.'

The next song was learned by Sally from her step-father. The tune has been made to serve for several other songs, including 'The Station Cook' or 'Fowler's Bay', in Australia.

THE KNICKERBOCKER LINE

Oh, I took a trip to Bristol in the train that's run by steam,
The dress my love was wearing was fit for any queen,
[Line forgotten]
With her high-heeled boots to rattle on the knickerbocker line.

CHORUS:
Twig her, pipe her, watch her how she goes,
Her high-heeled boots and patent leather, my Jinny she's on the
go;
She is one of the fast girls, her beauty is bound to shine,
With her high-heeled boots to rattle on the knickerbocker line.

My love she is a tailoress, a tailoress be trade,
And many a coat and wes'coat my love for me has made.
She rises in the morning and finishes off in time,
With her high-heeled boots to rattle on the knickerbocker line.

'Young Molly Bán' (ballad no. 29 in *Irish Street Ballads*) is the same song as Sally Sloane's 'Molly Baun Lavery', with only a few slight differences in text and some similarity in tune.

MOLLY BAUN LAVERY

Come all you young fellows that follow the gun,
Beware of going a-shooting by the late setting sun,
It might happen to anyone, as it happened to me,
To shoot your own true love in under a tree.

She was going to her uncle, when the shower it came on;
She went under a bush, the rain for to shun.
With her apron all around her, I took her for a swan,
And I levelled my gun and I shot Molly Baun.

I ran to her uncle in haste and great fear,
Saying, 'Uncle, dear uncle, I've shot Molly dear.
With her apron all around her, I took her for a swan,
But oh, alas, it was my own Molly Baun.

'I shot my own true love, alas, I'm undone,
While she was in the shade by the setting of the sun.
If I thought she was there, I'd caress her tenderly,
And soon I'd get married to my own Molly dear.'

My curse on you, Toby, that lent me your gun,
To go out a-shooting by the late setting sun.
I rubbed her fair temples, and found she was dead,
A fountain of tears for my Molly I shed.

Up came my aged father, and his locks they are grey,
'Stay here in your own country, and don't run away.
Stay in your own country till your trial it comes on,
And I'll see you're set free by the laws of the land.'

All the maids of this country they will all be glad
When they hear the sad news that my Molly is dead.
Take them all in their hundreds, set them all in a row,
Molly Baun she'll shine like a mountain of snow.

The song recorded by Ron Manton as 'Mrs McGrath'—and usually known by that title—is called 'My Son Ted' by Sally Sloane. Her mother learned the song in the Parkes district and taught it to Sally. As was mentioned earlier, Colm O Lochlainn prints a very similar song in his *Irish Street Ballads*.

MY SON TED

'Oh, Mrs McGrath,' the sergeant said,
'Would you like to make a soldier out of your son Ted?
With a scarlet coat and a big red hat,
Now, Mrs McGrath, wouldn't you like that?'
With a too-ri-ra, fol-the-riddle-da,
Ri-fol-the-riddle-dolly-di-do.

So Mrs McGrath lived on the seashore
For a space of seven long years or more,
Till she saw a big ship sailing into the bay—
'Here's my son Ted, wisha, clear the way!'
With a too-ri-ra, etc.

'Oh, Captain dear, wherever you be,
Have you been sailing over the Mediterranean,
Or have ye any tidings of my son Ted?
Is the poor boy living, or is he dead?'
With a too-ri-ra, etc.

Then up comes Ted without any legs,
And in their place he has two wooden pegs.
She kissed him a dozen times or two,
Saying, 'Holy Moses, is it you!'
With a too-ri-ra, etc.

'Oh, then, were ye drunk or were ye blind
That ye left your two fine legs behind?
Or was it walking upon the sea
Wore your two fine legs from your knees?'
With a too-ri-ra, etc.

197

'Oh, I wasn't drunk and I wasn't blind
That I left my two fine legs behind,
For a cannon-ball on the fifth of May
Took my two fine legs from the knees away.'
With a too-ri-ra, etc.

'Oh, then, Teddy my boy,' the widow cried,
'Your two fine legs were your mumma's pride.
Them stumps of a tree wouldn't do at all.
Why didn't you run from the big cannon-ball?'
With a too-ri-ra, etc.

'All foreign wars I do proclaim,
Between Don John and the King of Spain,
And by heavens I'll make them rue the time
That they swept the legs from a child of mine.'
With a too-ri-ra, etc.

'Oh, then, if I had you back again,
I'd never let you go to fight the King of Spain,
For I'd rather my Ted as he used to be,
Than the King of France and his whole navee.'
With a too-ri-ra, etc.

In the seven years John Meredith recorded Sally Sloane he gathered over 150 items. Many are fragments, but most of these are complete as regards tune. The greater proportion of her repertoire came from her grandmother and is made up of Irish versions of old songs, but there is a goodly mixture of bush songs thrown in. She knows a few music-hall and more old popular songs. On fiddle, accordion, and mouthorgan she has played dozens of old dance tunes for John Meredith—set tunes for the lancers and quadrilles, jigs, hornpipes, reels, waltzes, polkas, mazurkas, and varsoviennas.

She has a quick memory for a tune and sings in traditional Irish style, with a hard clear voice, utterly devoid of any artificiality, although sometimes when singing an art song she falls away into concert soprano style. Sally Sloane is complete master of her medium, weaving melody and words into a complex of sound that is spellbinding. She takes a phrase, and, like a Chinese dancer with a red silk scarf, throws it into the air, drawing the words down through the melody in a smooth sinuous arpeggio that beggars description.

Noah Warren

Noah Warren worked on the open-cut coalmine at Wallerawang, near Lithgow. For John Meredith he sang 'Australia's On the Wallaby', which Joe Young, a fellow worker, learned in Cairns and was frequently requested to sing at local socials. Noah asked Joe for a copy of the words, but, like many folk-singers, Joe wanted to keep exclusive possession of the song. The song was then called for as often as possible at socials and Workmen's Club functions, and each time Joe sang it Noah would furtively attempt to copy down the words on cigarette packets and scraps of paper. Eventually, Noah managed to memorize the verses. Joe relented, and now the two men sing it as a duet!

AUSTRALIA'S ON THE WALLABY

Our fathers came to search for gold,
The claim it proved a duffer.
The syndicates and bankers' bosses
Made us all suffer.
We're all for freedom for ourselves,

Ourselves, our mates of toil.
Australia's sons are weary
And the billy's on the boil.

CHORUS:

Australia's on the wallaby,
Listen to the cooee.
The kangaroo he packs his port
And the emu shoulders bluey.
The boomerangs are whizzing round,
The dingo scratches gravel,
And the possum, bear and the bandicoot
Are always on the travel.

Of tiger-snakes and dampers—
That's what's on the coals—
Droughts and floods and ragged duds
And dried-up water-holes,
Shadeless gums and sun-scorched plains;
They're asking us to toil.
Australia's sons are weary
And the billy's on the boil.

The kooka calls, the bats and owl,
The pigeons and the shag.
The platypus and the mallee hens
Are rolling up their swags.
The curlew waves his hand goodbye
Beside the long lagoon,
And the brolga does his last lay waltz
To the lyrebird's mocking tune.

As mentioned earlier, the music of the above song is a variant of the tune used in northern Queensland for Lawson's 'Freedom on the Wallaby', and also for Jim Bourke's 'Mazlim's Mill'.

Chris Williams

Chris Williams, an ex-shearer, seemed to prefer recitation to singing and treated Meredith to two of his cleaner versions. Both are better known as songs, and both can be printed only in part.

He was boasting of his shearing,
Up in Jimmy Holman's bar—
A pale and puny little chap,
As big guns mostly are.
He'd rung some sheds of a larger scale
Away on the Queensland side,
And tried to murder Hogan,
Who retained a lot of pride.

'You're a bloody f- - - -n' liar!'
Up spoke Hogan straight and blunt.
'You louse-bound little bastard,
You was never in the front.'
And up jumped Jacky Blowhard,
Who reeked of camel-dung,
Just lobbed from the wild Monaro,
Where women eat their young.

He said, 'Now, boys, don't quarrel,
There's beer here for the crowd.
We could sit down peacefully
And voice our tallies loud.'
But Blowhard had no tallies,
He had nothing to detail;
He simply dreamed of beery revels
Along the camel trail.
[Remaining 4 verses deleted]

The second offering was 'The Union Girl'.

THE UNION GIRL

I was fishing on the Macquarie once
And couldn't get a bite;
While strolling round some worms to seek
I saw a pretty sight.

Beneath a shady old gumtree
I saw a loving pair,
The bloke was doing his level best
To get a nice cadare [sic].

He said, 'I am a shearer, love,
Those unions I don't like.
I'll make a ton of money
While those bastards are out on strike.

'All my scab-earned money
With you I'll freely share.
Roll over on your back, my love,
And we'll have a nice cadare.'
[Remaining 3 verses deleted]

Williams also sang 'The Drover's Dream' for Meredith.

THE DROVER'S DREAM

Whilst travelling with some sheep,
While my mates were fast asleep,
Not a star or moon beneath the southern sky.
I was dozing, I suppose,
For my eyes were hardly closed,
When a very strange procession passed me by.
First there came a kangaroo,
With a swag of blankets blue,
A dingo followed closely for a mate.
They saluted me and passed,
They were travelling very fast,
Saying, 'Let us jog along, it's getting late.'

When the old bandicoot
Played a tune upon the flute,
A frilled-neck lizard listened with a smile.
An emu standing near
With its claw up to its ear
Said, 'That's the sweetest thing I've heard for quite a while.'

An opossum [sic] and a crow
Sang a song of long ago;
Three native bears came in and formed a ring;
The pelican and the crane
Came in from off the plain
And amused the audience with an 'ighland fling.

Three frogs from off the swamp,
Where the atmosphere was damp,
Came hopping in and sat upon some stones.
They laid down their swags
And took from out their bags
The violin, the banjo and the bones.
Then there came an awful crash,
As though creation had gone smash!
Waking up, I found I'd been asleep,
And the boss beneath the cart
He gave me an awful start,
He said, 'Dreamy, where the f---g hell's the sheep?'

Bill Shawcross

John Meredith searched for a long time for someone who knew
'The Spider from the Gwydir', referred to in Victoria as 'The
Redbacked Spider'. Finally, he was told to try old Bill Shawcross. Bill had heard it, as had many Lithgow residents, but
could not remember the words. However, he did have a recitation called 'Kelly Was Their Captain'.

KELLY WAS THEIR CAPTAIN

Come all you wild colonial boys and attention to me pay,
For in my song I will unfold the truth without delay.
'Twas of a famous outlawed band that roamed this country round,
Ned Kelly was their captain and no better could be found.

But the Governor of Victoria was an enemy of this man,
And a warrant he likewise put out to take his brother Dan.
But, alas, one day some troopers came young Dan to apprehend,
And he like a tiger stood at bay, his mother to defend.

Five hundred pounds reward was made for Ned, where'er was found,
And from place to place was hunted as if he was a hound.
Now driven to desperation to the bush brave Ned did take,
Young Dan, Steve Hart and brave Joe Byrne, all for his mother's sake.

And although they deemed them outlaws, brave men they proved to be,
And vengeance ranked [sic] in every breast for Kelly's misery.
They burnt his mother's vine-clad hut, which caused his heart to yearn,
And angered his companions, Dan, Steve Hart and brave Joe Byrne.

One day as Ned and his comrades in ambush were concealed
They spied three mounted troopers and their presence did reveal.
They called to them 'Surrender!' These words to them he said,
'Resist a man among you and I'll surely shoot you dead.'

Now Kennedy, Scanlon and Lonergan in death were lying low,
When Ned amongst them recognized his old and vitrous [?vicious]
 foe;
Then thoughts came of his mother with a baby at her breast,
And it filled Ned's heart with anger and the country knows the rest.

It was at the Wombat Ranges where Ned Kelly made his haunt,
And all those Victorian troopers at that name would truly daunt.
For months they lay in ambush until finally were betrayed
By traitor Aaron Sherritt, and his life the treachery paid.

It was at the Glenrowan station where the conflict raged severe,
When more than fifty policemen at the scene then did appear.
No credit to their bravery, no credit to their name,
Ned Kelly terrified them all and put their blood to shame.

Bill Shawcross died a month after he had recorded the ballad.

R. J. Blumer

As already mentioned, several men knew of, or were able to recite
a few bawdy lines from, a version of 'The Spider from the Gwydir'
not yet located. The words given below were taken from an old
notebook compiled by R. J. Blumer and now in the possession of
his son, Eric Blumer, who lives at Vale of Clwydd, a suburb of
Lithgow.

THE SPIDER FROM THE GWYDIR

By the sluggish River Gwydir
Lived a wicked redbacked spider,
He was just about as vicious as could be;
And the place that he was camped in
Was a rusty Jones's jam-tin,
In a paddock by the showground at Moree.
Near him lay a shearer snoozing,
He had been on the grog and boozing
All the night and all the previous day,

And the 'kooking' of the kookas
And the noise of showground spruikers
Failed to wake him from the trance in which he lay.
Then a crafty looking spieler
With a dainty little sheila
Came along collecting wood to make a fire;
Said the spieler, 'There's a boozer
And he's going to be a loser.
If he isn't, you can christen me a liar!
Wriggle round and keep nit, honey,
While I fan the mug for money,
And we'll have some luxuries for tea.'
She answered, 'Don't be silly!
You go back and boil the billy:
You can safely leave the mug to little me.'
So she circled ever nearer
Till she reached the dopey shearer,
With his pocket bulging, fast asleep and snug;
But she didn't see the spider
That was ringing just beside her,
For her mind was on the money and the mug.
Now the spider wanted dinner,
He was daily growing thinner,
He'd been fasting and was hollow as an urn;
As she eyed the bulging pocket
He just darted like a rocket
And he bit the spieler's sheila on the stern.
Like a flash she raced off squealing
And her clothes began unpeeling
While to hear her yells would make you feel forlorn;
On the bite one hand was pressing
While the other was undressing
And she reached the camp the same as she was born.
Then the shearer, pale and haggard,
Woke, and back to town he staggered,
Where he caught the train and gave the booze a rest,
And he'll never know a spider
That was camping by the Gwydir
Had saved him sixty-seven of the best.

Muriel Whalan

Although reared on a small farm named Coolcappa at Sunny
Corner, a village on the road from Lithgow to Bathurst, Muriel

Whalan now lives at Katoomba in the Blue Mountains. As a girl, she learned several songs from her mother, Mrs J. Egan, when the family was gathered round the open fireplace on cold winter's nights.

Muriel Whalan sings a fragment of 'Tambaroora Gold'—as do numbers of persons, but none has yet been able to record a complete text.

TAMBAROORA GOLD

Oh, she was such a nice young girl,
Just seventeen years old,
And she scooted away with a man
With plenty of Tambaroora gold.

Another fragment, with just sufficient of the words to cover the tune, was the 'Ballad of the Drover'.

BALLAD OF THE DROVER

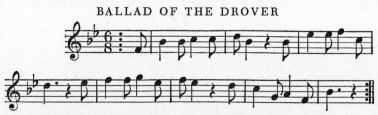

Across the stony ridges; across the rolling plain,
Young Harry Dale, the drover, comes riding home again.
And well his stock-horse bears him, and light of heart is he,
And stoutly his old packhorse is trotting by his knee.

[2 lines omitted]
He hums a song of someone he hopes to marry soon;
And hobble-chains and camp-ware are jingling to the tune.

206

Mrs Whalan was the only person found by John Meredith who sang 'The Pommy's Lament'. 'Banjo' Paterson printed a version ('The Beautiful Land of Australia') in his *Old Bush Songs* (1905), but broadside copies dating back to 1842 have been recently discovered.

THE POMMY'S LAMENT

All you on emigration bent,
With home and England discontent,
Come, listen to my sad lament
About the bush of Australia.

CHORUS:
Illawarra, Mittagong,
Parramatta, Wollongong.
If you wish to become an orang-outang—
Well, go to the bush of Australia.

Once I possessed a thousand pounds.
Says I to meself, How grand it sounds
For a man to be farming his own grounds
In the promising land of Australia!

When coming out the ship got lost,
In a very sad plight we reached the coast,
And very nearly made a roast
For the savages of Australia.

Escaped from thence I lighted on
A fierce bushranger with his gun,
Who borrowed my garments, every one,
For himself in the bush of Australia.

207

Sydney Town we reached at last.
Says I to meself, All danger's passed;
Now I'll make me fortune fast
In the promising land of Australia.

So off I went with cash in hand,
Upon the map I bought my land,
But found it naught but barren sand
When I got to the bush of Australia.

Of sheep I got a famous lot,
Some died of hunger, some of rot;
But the divil a lot of rain we got
In this promising land of Australia.

My convicts they were always drunk,
And kept me in a mighty funk,
Says I to meself as to bed I sunk,
I wish I were out of Australia.

Of ills I've had enough, you'll own,
But something else my woes to crown,
One night my bark hut tumbled down
And settled me in Australia.

Of cash and homestead thus bereft,
The ruddy spot I gladly left,
Making it over by deed of gift
To the savages of Australia.

Now stones upon the road I break,
And earn my seven bob a week.
'Tis better surely than the freak
Of settling down in Australia.

'It was during the depression days,' Mrs Whalan remarked when introducing the song 'Sergeant Small', 'and there was a detective by the name of Sergeant Small, and he used to get into the trains when the travellers were jumping the rattler. He'd get in the trains and pretend that he also was a traveller, a bagman, and jump the rattler with them. Quite a number of them were arrested for jumping the rattler through Sergeant Small, and a chap wrote this song about him. I can't remember all of it.'

Several others sing the same few lines, so possibly it is only a very brief song.

Oh, I wish I were about fourteen stone
And only six foot tall.
I'd take the train back north,
Just to beat up Sergeant Small.

The Blackman Family

Arthur Davis of Cullenbone, a hamlet half-way between Mudgee and Gulgong, introduced John Meredith to the local residents, including his uncle, George Davis. His cousin, Keith Stapleton, was living in the same house and introduced Meredith to his aunts, the Misses Clara and Margaret Stapleton.

Then Arthur took John to see his wife's aunt, Mrs Smeed, a daughter of Tom Blackman (senior), a noted fiddler and concertina player. Mrs Keith Stapleton was a granddaughter of this particular Blackman. Mrs Smeed and her brother, also named Tom, were grandchildren, and Mrs Keith Stapleton was a great grandchild, of the man who was one of the discoverers of Cudgegong valley and one of the first settlers in the Mudgee district in the early part of the nineteenth century.

The relationship between all these informants is rather involved, as is the history of some of the tunes they play. These tunes have developed many variants, to the extent that everyone thinks his or hers is the correct version and nobody is quite sure who learned what from whom. Nevertheless, much of the music and some of the songs still sung in Mudgee date back to the original Tom Blackman.

Margaret Stapleton, aged seventy, sang 'A Bushman's Song' for John Meredith. She does not like the tunes of the bush songs; they are dull and uninteresting, she says, in comparison with such 'nice' songs as 'Loch Lomond' and 'Grannie's Highland Home'. She learned 'A Bushman's Song' from her father and said that 'Banjo' Paterson, who was a friend of her father, used to sing it to him. An identical version is in an old notebook compiled by Keith Stapleton's father, Margaret's brother. It is interesting to note the line 'His brand's the Rouse's R . . .', as Rouse was also an early settler in the Mudgee district.

A BUSHMAN'S SONG

I'm travelling down the Castlereagh and I'm a station hand,
I'm handy with a roping pole, I'm handy with the brand;
And I can ride a rowdy colt or swing an axe all day,
But there's no demand for a station hand along the Castlereagh.

> So it's shift, boys, shift—for there isn't the slightest doubt
> We had to make a shift to a station further out;
> With the packhorse running after, he followed like a dog.
> We strike across the country at the old jig-jog.

This old black horse I'm riding, you notice what's his brand;
His brand's the Rouse's R, you'll see—none better in the land.
He takes a lot of beating; the other day we tried,
For a bit of a joke with a racy bloke, for twenty pound a side.

> So it's shift, boys, shift—for there isn't the slightest doubt
> We had to make a shift for the money was nearly out,
> But he cantered home a winner, with the other at the flog—
> He's a red-hot sort to pick up with his old jig-jog.

I asked a cove for shearing once down on the Marthaguy:
'We shear non-union here,' said he. 'I'll leave you then,' said I.
I looked along the shearing shed before I turned to go—
There was four and twenty Chinamen a-shearing in a row.

210

So it was shift, boys, shift—for there isn't the slightest doubt
We had to make a shift when there's Chinamen about.
So we saddled up the horses, and we whistled to the dogs,
And we crossed a lot of country at the old jig-jog.

The second song recorded by 'Auntie' Margaret is of the 'stage-Irish' kind; it also was learned from her father.

THE LOVE-OF-GOD SHAVE

It was in this 'ere town and not far from the spot
That a barber once opened a snug little shop.
He was so good-tempered and his smiles were so sweet
It is said that he coaxed people out of the street.

CHORUS:
> *With your lather and shave, and lather and shave,*
> *And lather and shave and dithery-wack.*

By chance a poor Irishman stole upon that way—
His beard had been growing for many a day.
He went into the barber's and threw down his hod,
Saying, 'Give us a shave for the pure love of God.'

'Toot, toot,' said the barber, 'I never give trust.'
'By grave,' then said Paddy, 'but this time you must.
For the divil a penny have I got to pay,
And I ain't had a shave for this many a day.'

'Sit down,' said the barber, 'sit down on this chair,
And I'll soon mow off your long grizzly beard to an 'air.'
With his lather all spread over Paddy's broad chin
With a rusty old razor the barber begin.

211

'Stop, stop!' said Paddy. 'What the divil are you doin'!
Leave off,' cried poor Pat, 'or my jaw you will ruin.
Who the divil could sit to be shaved by a saw!
Leave off, or you'll drag every tooth in my jaw.'

'Sit still,' said the barber. 'Don't make such a din,
For you'll surely be cut by the move of your chin.'
'Cut!' said Pat. 'Why that razor you've got
It wouldn't cut butter, nay if it was hot.'

The job it was done. 'Well,' said Pat, 'that's a tazer;
If it's a love-of-God shave, it's the divil's own razor.
For my part, you can shave all your friends till you're sick,
But I'd just as soon be shaved with a brick.'

One day as poor Paddy was passing the door
He heard an old donkey giving a roar.
He says to himself, There's that vagabond Dave
Givin' another poor divil a love-of-God shave.

Keith Stapleton recites 'When Carbine Won the Cup' in a sing-song manner that approximates that of a racing commentator describing a race. This ballad, about what many consider to have been the greatest of all Melbourne Cups, was learned from the notebook previously mentioned.

WHEN CARBINE WON THE CUP

The race was run, the Cup was won,
The great event was o'er.
The grandest horse e'er trod a course
Has led them home once more.
I watched with pride his sweeping stride
Before they ranged in line,
As far and near a ringing cheer
Was echoed for Carbine.

The start was made, no time delayed
Before they got away.
Those horses great, some thirty-eight,
Were eager for the fray.
No better start could human heart
To sportsmen ever show.
Watson bid, each jockey did
Get ready, forward, go!

With lightning speed each gallant steed
Along the greensward tore.
Each rider knew what he must do
To finish in the fore.
But Ramage knew his mount was true
Although he'd ten five up,
For Musket's son had great deeds done
Before this Melbourne Cup.

No whip, no spur, he needs to stir
The horse to greater speed,
Who knows as well as man can tell
When he must take the lead.
So on he glides with eager strides
Although he's led by nine.
His rider knows before the close
He'll try them with Carbine.

The bend is past, the straight at last,
He takes him to the fore.
The ringing crowd with voices loud
The brave steed's name now roar.
The jockey now full well did know
The race was nearly o'er.
On his mane he slacked the rein
No need to urge him more.

The brave horseman that led the van
On that November day,
Your record will live in history still
When you have passed away.
For such a race for weight and pace
No more we'll see put up
Than what was done by Musket's son
In the eighteen-ninety Cup.

A fragment of schooldays returned in Keith's recitation 'The Girls of Ulan'. Ulan is a village up on the Great Divide, some twenty miles north-east of Mudgee.

THE GIRLS OF ULAN

The girls from Ulan
Need no schoolin'
For blucher boots are all the go.
And how their hobnail boots they rattle

On that hard and slippery floor,
Like a mob of Queensland cattle
On the rush at four. . . .

Dolly Smeed recorded 'As I Was a-Walking' for John Meredith. The words are much the same as in Ina Popplewell's version.

AS I WAS A-WALKING

As I was a-walking one morning in June,
For to view the fair fields and the meadows in bloom,
I viewed a fair damsel, she appeared like some queen,
With her costly fine robes round her mantle so green.

I said, 'My fair damsel, if you'll gang with me
We'll both join in wedlock and married we'll be.
I'll dress you so richly as you'll appear like some queen,
With the costly fine robes round the mantle so green.'

'Oh, young man, oh, young man, you must be refused,
For I'll wed with no man, I must be excused.
I'll wander those wild woods for to shed all men's view,
Since the lad I love dearly is in famed Waterloo.'

'If your true love's in battle, pray tell me his name,
For I've been in battle, I might know the same.'
'Draw near to my garment and there you will see
It is all wrote in 'broidery round me mantle so green.'

At the rising of her garment, oh! there I behold
His love name and his surname in letters of gold.
'If Willie O'Reilly it was your true lover's name,
He was my chief comrade in famed Waterloo.

'We fought there for three days; on the fourth afternoon
He received his death warrant on the eighteenth of June.
And as he was dying, I heard his last cry,
'Twas, "Me own darling Nancy, if I'm 'tented to die."

'Oh, Nancy, oh, Nancy, I've won your heart,
In your own father's garden where first we did part.
In your own father's garden under yon shady green tree
Where we hoping held hands, and your mantle so green.'

Those couple got married, I've heard people say,
And were both well attended on their wedding day;
For peace was proclaimed and the wars they were o'er
To your own darling Nancy, you are welcome once more.

Like several of the other older ballad-singers recorded by
John Meredith, Mrs Smeed spoke the last three syllables '—*come
once more*'.

She recalled only three verses of 'The Banks of the Riverine'
when Meredith was recording in Mudgee. Incidentally, she
pronounced Riverine as River Rhine.

THE BANKS OF THE RIVERINE

'Oh, hark the dogs are barking, love, and I must be away;
The chaps they have gone mustering, I heard the shepherds say,
And I must heave the anchor for it's many a weary mile
For to meet the Victorian shearers on the banks of Riverine.'

215

'Oh, Willie, dearest Willie, don't leave me here behind;
You'll curse and rue the very day since first you went away.
Though parting with my own true love's like parting with my life,
So turn and be a selector, love, and I will be your wife.

'Those yellow locks I will cut off, men's clothing I'll put on,
I'll dress in moleskin trousers, love, and be a shearer too;
I'll shear and keep your tally, love, whilst shearing you do shine,
And I'll wash your greasy moleskins on the banks of Riverine.'

Mrs Smeed's brother, distinguished by John Meredith as Tom Blackman junior although in his seventies, played an unnamed jig on his fiddle. This must have been popular in the bush in bygone days, for it has been collected from other performers, including Sally Sloane and Joe Cashmere.

JIG

A schottische tune, 'Navvy on the Line', was particularly popular with men at country dances, since most of them knew the bawdy words. Tom Blackman junior said the men would often request this or 'Ivan Skivinsky Skivar', and then dance around to the music with silly grins on their faces.

Tom's version of 'The Mudgee Schottische', which he played on the accordion, is somewhat similar to that of Jim Lyons of Cook's Gap (see p. 236).

I'm a nipper, I'm a ripper,
I'm a navvy on the line,
I get four and twenty bob a week
Besides me overtime.
All the ladies love the navvies
And the navvies love the fun,
There'll be plenty little babies
When the railway's done.

Some like the girls
Who are slender in the waist,
Others like the girls
Who are pretty in the face.
But give me the girl
Who'll take it in her fist
And shove it right home
Into the cuckoo's nest.

Yet another varsovienna came from Tom Blackman junior. This was learned from his father.

VARSOVIENNA

George Davis

The 'Sailor's Hornpipe' has long been popular with solo step-dancers. There are many varying tunes for the dance. The one reproduced here was played on a button accordion by Arthur

Davis's uncle, George Davis, when he was seventy-eight.

George Davis was quite sprightly when recorded and played all his tunes, most of which he learned in the Hargraves district from 1890 onwards, in brisk dance tempo.

SAILOR'S HORNPIPE

One waltz tune, learned by George Davis at Grattai, near Hargraves, when he was a young man, owes its unusual title to the fact that it used to be played by a German miner named 'Spookendyke' (called 'Strike-a-light' by the other diggers).

SPOOKENDYKE'S WALTZ

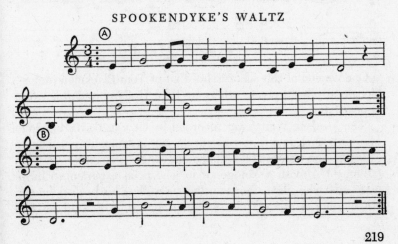

219

There are two tunes known to most Mudgee musicians that have never been encountered elsewhere. They have apparently descended from goldfields musicians and have not been dispersed, although many variations exist throughout the district. A study of these tunes in their variants may provide useful clues to the origin of variants, as obviously all present-day performers must ultimately have learned the tunes from a single source. As neither tune has a name, John Meredith has called them 'The Mudgee Schottische' and 'The Mudgee Waltz' respectively. Sally Sloane says the schottische bears a resemblance to a tune she used to know as 'The Belle Brandon Schottische'.

George Davis's version follows.

THE MUDGEE SCHOTTISCHE

One version of this schottische—that of Tom Blackman junior—has already been given; others by Fred Holland and Jim Lyons appear later.

'The Mudgee Waltz' was recorded by George Davis, but John Meredith first heard it played on an instrument peculiar to Mudgee, the kerosene-tin dulcimer, which was made by Cyril ('Bunny') Abbott, a Mudgee man who is an experienced bushman—and who plays the accordion as well as his bush dulcimer. He learned it from Tom Blackman junior, who said he had

learned it from his father. At first Meredith thought he should
call it 'The Tom Blackman Waltz', but Fred Holland mentioned
that he had taught it to Blackman senior years before.

The kerosene-tin dulcimer consisted of a four-gallon tin with
sound-holes cut into the ends and a broom-handle neck. Strung
with three steel-guitar strings in a fairly high register, the dulcimer had a bridge at each end. Two of the three strings were
tuned in unison, and the third, for some unknown reason, was
sharpened slightly. The method of playing used was strumming
with a plectrum and stopping in unison with a steel-guitar 'steel'
or similarly shaped piece of iron. The effect was rather like that
produced when a banjo-mandolin is played in unison with a
fiddle.

THE MUDGEE WALTZ
(Cyril Abbott's version)

There are two important variations: in one, which Fred Holland insisted was the correct one, most of the notes are of equal
value (and the tune is played in what he called a 'running
style'), and in the other dotted crochets are followed by a quaver
or semi-quavers, giving the tune a jerky movement.

George Davis played the tune in 'running style' on the button accordion.

THE MUDGEE WALTZ
(George Davis's version)

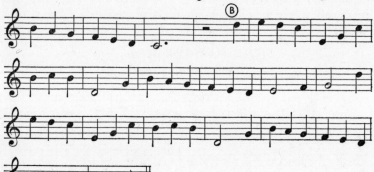

'The Heel and Toe Polka' was learned by Davis when a lad of nine or ten years of age. Years ago John Meredith heard the same tune played as an accompaniment for a Russian dance group. In its original form the tune is that of a Polish polka-type dance called the krakowiak or cracoviak.

THE HEEL AND TOE POLKA

222

Arthur Davis

Arthur Davis was born at Avisford on Meroo Creek, an alluvial goldfield about twenty miles from Mudgee and four miles from Hargraves. George Davis and his brother (Arthur's father) worked together as goldminers at Avisford. George died in Mudgee in 1959.

Arthur recited 'The Warrego Lament' for John Meredith. His version should be compared with the ballad as sung by Sally Sloane.

A. L. Lloyd (in the *Journal of the English Folk Dance and Song Society*) has stated that miscegenation is a topic usually avoided in Australian folk song, but 'The Warrego Lament' is typical of a large number of songs that refute this view. Most of the songs dealing with miscegenation do not lend themselves to un-expurgated publication.

THE WARREGO LAMENT

Have you ever been up in Queensland?
If you have you'll know the same
Turned [Town] out upon the Warrego—
Cunnamulla is its name.
I fell in love with a pretty girl there,
I'll have you all to know.
She was black—but what of that?—
Queen of the Warrego.

She was just the sort for a bushman,
She'd drink rum and she'd smoke,
In her hand she carried the boomerang,
She wore the possum cloak.
She yabbered to me, 'O boodgeree,
You am belong to me.
Bin sposum you gibbit me shillin'
Me cock 'em up boodgeree.'

I paid in the shilling,
A youthful fool and flash,
And things went right for a week or two,
Then I found I had a dose.
I went to an old quack doctor,
And I was forced to go,
And I lost the head of me beantosser
Out on the Warrego.

Mick and Tom Brennan

Mick Brennan was born at Birriwa in 1892. His father was an Irish immigrant who was particularly proud of the fact that he had not been assisted in any way in coming to Australia. Mick worked as a shearer most of his life. During his youth at Birriwa he learned 'Ye Landlords of Ireland' from an Irish-Australian named Wild.

YE LANDLORDS OF IRELAND

I went unto America, that sweet land of the free,
But in short years after I returned
Back to my native land.
To hear the news the good priest told to me,
It caused my heart to mourn—
My mother in the poorhouse died
And I had crossed the sea.
It was then a fearful venom seized me.
With my right hand to my bosom,
With my left hand raised on high,
I swore by my creator
That that cruel 'victed [evicting] landlord
He must surely die.
The night was dark and stormy,
The trigger drew, the tyrant slew,
His soul I sent to hell.
That turned me to a wanderer
Far from my native land.
That when the day of judgment comes,
When all our race is run,
May God forgive the venom shown
By that poor old widow's son.
So, you landlords of Ireland,
No matter where you be,
Oh, meet your fate as he did
And old Ireland will be free.

224

The American lands are helping,
Their eagle, gold and wings,
And the harp of dear old Ireland's
Just a mass of broken strings.

Tom Brennan is the son of Mick and was forty-four when recorded singing 'On the Steps of the Dole Office Door'. The song was learned during the depression of the 1930s. Mudgee had a reputation as a hard town for the unemployed in those bitter days.

ON THE STEPS OF THE DOLE OFFICE DOOR

The songs that we sang
Were about old Jack Lang
On the steps of the Dole Office door.
He closed up the banks,
It was one of his pranks,
And he sent us to the Dole Office door.
We molested the police
Till they gave us relief
On the steps of the Dole Office door.

His father remembered a few lines of another song of the depression, but not the tune:

I'm down and out and I mooch about
With my faith in things destroyed,
And I creep at night to the friendly light
Of the camp of the unemployed.

Tom's other song was a version of 'The Dying Stockman' which he learned as a schoolboy.

P

A strapping young stockman lay dying,
His saddle supporting his head;
His comrades around him were crying
When he rose on his pillow and said:

'If I had the wings of a bronzewing
Over the hills I would fly;
I'd fly to the scenes of my childhood
And there I'd be willing to die.

'Wrap me up with my stockwhip and blanket,
And bury me deep down below,
Where the dingoes and crows won't molest me,
In the shade where the coolabahs grow.'

Morrie Burchell

On the occasion of The Bushwhackers' visit to Mudgee to take part in a Henry Lawson commemoration concert, the band stayed at the Oriental Hotel. During the afternoon an impromptu recital of songs and music took place. A number of the local singers and instrumentalists took part: Vince and Keith Holland (p. 230) gave duets on accordions, Lindsay Carr (p. 239) played mouthorgan and piano, and a young fellow called Morrie Burchell sang 'Duck-foot Sue'.

'Duck-foot Sue' was recorded by Alan Scott, who kindly passed over a dubbing of his recording. Morrie Burchell, then aged about thirty years, has not been visited since that day.

Now I'm going to sing to you
About a girl I love so true,
She's chief engineer with the White Star line,
And her name is Duck-foot Sue.
She's got teeth like bits of pipe,
And a tongue like a yard of tripe,
And great big goo-goo eyes
Like plums before they're ripe.

She's one of the upper crust
And marry that girl I must,
For she said with a sigh,
As she said goodbye,
If you don't marry me I'll bust.
I took her to a party,
A fat man's social club,
It cost me half a dollar
To fill her up with grub.

Nor either is she fat,
Nor either is she lean,
She's just like a straw in a barrel of gin
When she's out on the backyard green.

Fred, Vince, and Keith Holland

Fred Holland was eighty-eight years old when recorded in
March 1957 and has since died. He lived all his life in the
Mudgee district as a bush worker. He played a concertina made
by John Stanley, the well-known maker of Bathurst. He had a
good repertoire of bush dance tunes, which he has passed on to
five of his six sons. The five who are musically minded are all
talented performers on button accordions and mouthorgans.

'White Man, Let Me Go' was learned in the late 1880s. It is a Canadian song which has rarely been heard in the country of its origin, so that it is most unusual to encounter it in Australia. The existence of an old goldfield called the Canadian Lead near Gulgong suggests that the song may have been brought to the district by Canadians during the rush to that field in the seventies.

Folk Songs of Canada, by E. F. Fowke and R. Johnston, includes a variant of this song with similar words, but to a tune in 2/4 time. A footnote reads: 'This plea of a captive Indian is obviously a white's man attempt to express the feelings of an Indian. Kenneth Peacock collected it from Philip Foley on the island of Fogo off the northeastern coast of Newfoundland in 1952, and Helen Creighton has also found it in Nova Scotia. It does not seem to have appeared in any published collection, and the Library of Congress has no information about it.'

WHITE MAN, LET ME GO

Let me go to the place that is far distant west,
To the place of my childhood, the place I love best.
Where long cedars grow and the bright waters flow
My parents would greet me—white man, let me go.

Let me go to the place where the cattle they play
In sight of my dwelling, so ancient and gay.
There dwells a fond mother, whose heart would overflow
At the sight of her boy—white man, let me go.

Let me go to those hills and valleys so fair,
Where oft-times I have breathed my own mountain air,
When oft through the forest with my quiver and bow
I have chased the wild deers—so, white man, let me go.

Let me go to my father, by whose valiant side,
Who taught me to fight in the height of my pride,

Who taught me to conquer the hillside and snow.
My father is a chief Indian—white man, let me go.

Let me go to that fair little Indian maid
Who taught me to love her beneath the willow's shade,
Whose heart is like the pine, it's as pure as the snow,
And she loves her young Indian—white man, let me go.

Let me go to the place that is far, far away,
No more shall I wander, no more shall I stray.
But there let my body and ashes lie low,
All on the wild forest—white man, let me go.

John Meredith found it difficult to record Fred Holland, because he lived with a son in a part of the country without an electric-power supply and rarely visited Mudgee. Dud Mills—a local pastoralist, who has published bush verse and is a virtuoso bones player and a good singer of bush songs—came to his assistance with a Landrover and an inverter, which would supply the required 240 volts AC from a car battery.

Gulgambee, the Holland homestead, was set in a deep valley surrounded by precipitous hills, some so steep that Meredith had to cling to the Landrover's crash-bar while the vehicle crept down headlong descents in double-reduced gear.

During the visit Fred Holland recorded the two very interesting dance tunes known as 'The Mudgee Waltz' and 'The Mudgee Schottische', both of which have already been discussed (pp. 220-2).

THE MUDGEE WALTZ

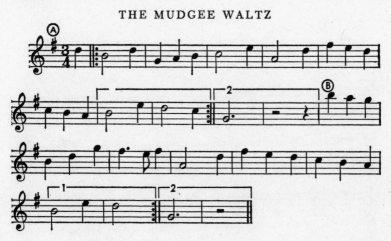

During the impromptu concert at the Oriental Hotel mentioned earlier, Keith and Vince Holland—Fred's sons—played a varsovienna which they had learned from their father. These two men were the best accordion players of the younger generation John Meredith met on his field trips; they had a quite characteristic style, a smooth sweeping one in perfect tempo for old-time dancing.

VARSOVIENNA

Also performed as a duo was another dance tune learned from their father, a polka-mazurka.

POLKA-MAZURKA

A schottische without a name, but a really effective tune, was recorded by Vince Holland.

SCHOTTISCHE

The schottische, as such, is rarely danced these days, but has been replaced by the barn dance of which it was a simplified form. However, the same tune can be used for both dances and many old schottische tunes are still played in country areas, particularly for the progressive barn dance.

Vince Holland learned 'The Harvest Moon Schottische' from his father. He plays this dance tune on the button accordion.

231

Ernie Sibley

John Meredith has recorded people in unusual surroundings, but none more peculiar than on the day when he had Ernie Sibley spouting verse in the laundry of the Oriental Hotel at Mudgee. Guests rightly objected to Meredith's having singers beefing out songs in his room, and the lounge was always occupied.

As in all stories worth their salt, everything turned out for the best—the power outlet in the laundry was alongside the beer garden. The recorder was balanced on the edge of the copper, and with Ernie perched on the tubs and 'Duke' Tritton fetching the beer the work proceeded happily.

The recitation 'Snakes' sounds as if it might belong to the Spencer-Goodge school of humorous balladry.

SNAKES

Reginald Alfonsus Bungy had a scientific mind,
From his earliest childhood was he taxidermically inclined.
Beasts and birds of many species gathered he from far and wide,

Crawliwigs and crows and spiders, goodness knows what else besides.
Reggy stuffed, preserved and mounted beetles, butterflies and bees,
Guinea-pigs and great goannas, fishes, finches, frogs and fleas.
He would roam by stream and scrubland, with his rod and gun and
    net,
Stalking, killing, skinning, stuffing every creature he could get.

In the noble cause of science, though his heart was far from hard,
Transfixed he poor dumb cockroaches through the vittles to a card.
Dawned the day at last when Reggy specimens of all near home
Had within his vast collection, then did he resolve to roam
Far afield for stranger creatures, painted parrot and grovelling grub,
Where the sportive bunyip gambols in the distant Wild Dog Scrub.

Now, old Wayback William was reflective as he trudged along the
    track,
With his blackened billy swinging, and his swag upon his back.
He was thinking deeply, sadly, for man is prone to actions rash,
And deplored the tantalizing slippiness of hard-earned cash.
Suddenly, with exclamations that I'd rather not repeat,
William stopped, and with a clatter dropped his billy at his feet.
'Well, spare my days!' said he, with other exclamations I'll omit.
'I-is this here a-a man afore me, or hupp-'ave I another fit?'

'Pardon me,' said Reggy Bungy—for 'twas none more strange than he—
'Pardon me, from your appearance, you're a native here I see.
May I glean some information of the fauna that abound
In this wild delightful woodland, and the countryside around?
For I'm a taxidermist.' 'A-a taxi-whatsi?' murmured Bill.
'Taxidermist,' answered Reggy, 'and I'll be grateful if you will
Tell me of some bird or reptile roaming in these parts you see
And I'll gladly pay for any information tendered me.'

'Reptiles,' pondered William. 'Reptiles. S-nakes, I s'pose, a-and lizards
    too?
W-well, look 'ere, mister, I could—I c'n put yer onto a squirming
    bloomin' zoo.
Reptiles—blimey! I see them by the thousands lately, mate!
Pink uns, blue uns, s-spotted red uns, sorts you'd never dream of,
    straight,
P-p-pup-purple snakes with crinkled stockin's, and yeller frogs with
    scarlet bands.
Crimson—hup—crimson rats an' cockerroaches standin' on their—hup—
    flamin' hands.

'Why, look! I-I see a blue goanna playin' circus with a hant.
S-spotted spiders chewin' damper, with their whiskers all aslant.
Hup—red-haired toads with greenish eyeballs, and—hup—their wes'-
    coats inside out.
Blue-neck-necked mice and pink death-adders chasin' catterworms
    about.
Why, look! I—hup—I see bald-headed ring-worms drinkin' horseshoes
    by the pint,
Whip-snakes kickin' crippled beetles, till their toes was out o' joint.

'Why, look! I—hup—' 'Oh, stop!' cried Reggy wildly. 'Have you met
    them in the scrub?'
'No-o-oh!' says Bill. ' 'Bout a—hup—mile on, up at Paddy Casey's pub.'
'Then,' said Reggy, 'I must call there when I come this way again.
Now I really must be moving. Don't you think it's going to rain?'
Handing Wayback Will a sovereign, wildly down the track he tore.
'S-struth' says William, turning pubward. 'Think I'll hup—go and
    see some more!'

Ernie Sibley is the possessor of an example of the wood-
carving of Paddy O'Rourke, a late Mudgee identity, also known
as 'Paddy the Rook', who used to carve little figures of Henry
Lawson from wood and sell them in hotels. Some of these
were in bas-relief and were made up as plaques, others were
carved into the end of whip-handles.

One day Sibley was sitting with Meredith in the beer garden
of the Oriental when he recalled the words of 'The Ryebuck
Shearer'; he did not know the tune. The four remembered verses
were taken down, and after another beer Ernie set off for home
on his pushbike. Ten minutes later he jumped off his bike and
breathlessly added the chorus that he had suddenly remembered
along the road. The stone referred to in the chorus is a Turkey
stone, a fine-textured oilstone for honing a fine edge to the
shears.

THE RYEBUCK SHEARER

I come from the south and my name it's Field,
And when my shears are properly steeled
A hundred and odd I have very often peeled,
And of course I'm a ryebuck shearer.

> *If I don't shear a tally before I go*
> *My shears and stone in the river I'll throw.*
> *I'll never open Sawbees to take another blow,*
> *And prove I'm a ryebuck shearer.*

> *There's a bloke on the board and I heard him say*
> *That I couldn't shear a hundred sheep a day,*
> *But some fine day I'll show him the way,*
> *And prove I'm a ryebuck shearer.*

> *Oh, I'll make a splash, but I won't say when,*
> *I'll hop off me tail and I'll into the pen,*
> *While the ringer's shearing five, I'll shear ten,*
> *And prove I'm a ryebuck shearer.*

> *There's a bloke on the board and he's got a yellow skin,*
> *A very long nose and he shaves on the chin,*
> *And a voice like a billygoat pissin' on tin,*
> *And of course he's a ryebuck shearer.*

Jim Lyons

Cook's Gap, not far from Ulan, had the reputation of producing good concertina players—most of whom now are dead.

John Meredith went to Cook's Gap equipped with a battery-operated recorder as well as his larger electrically operated apparatus. Jim Lyons, then in his seventies, was to be the first performer, but the recorder broke down. The nearest power supply was ten miles farther along the road at Ulan, and after lunch at a farmhouse a move was made towards the township.

The lady of the only house connected with the new power station was about to leave for church when the group called. Meredith explained his predicament, the lady smiled kindly, and ushered the song-collector and his troop—Arthur Davis and his son Les, 'Duke' Tritton, Jim Lyons and Fred Large—into the house. Telling them to make themselves at home, she went on her way.

Jim played a few tunes, including a variant of 'The Mudgee Schottische', and sang an incomplete version of 'The Broken-down Squatter'.

THE MUDGEE SCHOTTISCHE

When he recorded 'The Broken-down Squatter' Jim Lyons sang the chorus fragment after the twelve lines of verse.

THE BROKEN-DOWN SQUATTER

Come, Stumpy, old man, let us push while we can;
Your mates in the paddocks are dead.
Let us bid farewell to Glen Eva's fair dell
In the place where your lordship was bred.

No more shall we muster the river for fats,
Nor speed o'er the Fourteen Mile Plain,
Nor dash through the scrub by the light of the moon
To view the old stockyards again.

Leave the slip panels down, it don't matter much now,
It's only the crow lives to see,
Perched high on a pine, now longing to dine
On a broken-down squatter like me.

FRAGMENT OF CHORUS:

And the merchants are all up a tree,
And the big bugs are called
From the Bankrupted Court.
Oh, what chance for a young broken-down squatter like me?

Fred Large

Fred Large has already been mentioned as one of John Meredith's Ulan group. His father, a noted bush songster and concertina player, made some Edison recordings in the 1920s or 1930s; these, although thought to be still in existence, have not been traced. Fred, who was about fifty when Meredith recorded him in 1959, plays a button accordion and also sings, as does his son, Les, who is also a reciter of bush ballads.

Fred was nervous at the prospect of facing the microphone, so before Meredith arrived a friend had been administering alcoholic sedatives in large doses. As a result, he was not able to play as well as usual or remember all his songs.

When, as described above, the mob arrived at Ulan in their search for electric power, they discovered that only two buildings had been connected with the supply. One was the pub, to

237

which their natural inclinations led them, but Fred admitted
that he had been 'barred' for some misdemeanour. So it was that
the six enjoyed the hospitality of the only house in the neighbourhood with electricity.

'The Noomanally Shore' was partly sung by Fred. Noomanally
is an interesting corruption of Eumerella or Neumerella.

THE NOOMANALLY SHORE

There's a happy little valley on that Noomanally shore,
Where I rode many long and happy days.
We have land free-selected, we have acres by the score,
Where I unyoke my bullocks from the dray.

To my bullocks I will say, wherever you may stray,
For you'll never be impounded any more;
While you're running, running, running on that duffered piece of
ground,
Free-selected on that Noomanally shore.

And when we get our home, to the neighbours we will say,
Well, won't we cut a dash,
For we'll laugh Mister Squatter and the Browns,
And when we get the stuff, oh, won't the squatters laugh—

'No, I've lorst it . . .' Fred concluded lamely.

At a country ball, the first of the 'set' or square dances was usually the quadrilles, which in time came to be known as 'the first set'. Most musicians have their own favourite tunes for each of the set dances, such as the quadrilles, the lancers, the alberts, or the waltz cotillion, the last being a very attractive set dance entirely in waltz time.

The lead-up is one figure of the quadrilles. Another figure, the Stockyards, which comes towards the end of the dance, eventually became a dance in its own right—an Australian version of the Circassian Circle. The lead-up tune played by Lindsay Carr is characteristic of the type of tune used for this part of the quadrilles.

THE FIRST SET (LEAD-UP TUNE)

The waltz tune 'Why Did She Leave Killarney?' was always known in the Meredith family as 'Liza's Waltz'. Later, John Meredith heard Jack Lee sing—

> *Why did my master sell me?*
> *Why did my master sell me?*
> *Why did my master sell me*
> *Upon my wedding-day?*

and 'Why Did My Master Sell Me?' was the title Lee gave to the tune. Tom Byrnes said that it was called 'Why Did They Sell Killarney?'.

Having come to look upon the tune as an old German waltz his father had learned on a droving trip, John Meredith was surprised to find that it might also be an American song about slavery, but even more surprised when a Lithgow Scots bagpiper, David Finlay, played the same tune and said it was named 'The Highland Cradle Song'.

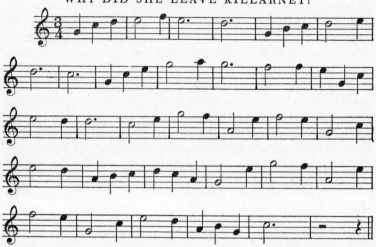

'My Father is a Dutchman', a waltz tune played on the mouthorgan by Lindsay Carr, was also recorded in Lithgow under the name of 'Little Willie Digby'. The same tune is used for a bawdy sea-song known variously as 'All the Nice Girls Love a Sailor' or 'Haul Away the Fore-t'-ga'nt S'ls'.

MY FATHER IS A DUTCHMAN

240

Mick Pilley

Mick Pilley's father taught his son to play the violin and most of his stock of tunes, he himself having been taught by an old Irish fiddler on the goldfields. The story is that this chap occasionally got so drunk he couldn't play his instrument properly. This upset him so much that he'd swear never to play again, and, to make certain, would chop the ends off his fingers with an axe. Sober again and filled with remorse, he would learn to play again with shortened fingers!

Pilley was considered by John Meredith to be the best fiddler he has met during his many field trips. He had a fine repertoire, played with a nice tone (just a little on the sharp side as all the best traditional fiddlers are), and had perfect dance tempo.

It was possibly due to his manner of playing, but his varsovienna tune is the most moving of all the tunes used for this dance.

VARSOVIENNA

As mentioned earlier, what Joe Cashmere knew as the 'Orphan Boy Waltz' was played by Mick Pilley, and his daughter Merle, as 'I've Got a Saviour That's Mighty to Keep'. Merle, who is what one might roughly call a traditional pianist, cannot read

Q

241

music and is self-taught, yet often played for local dances and plays and sings in a Mudgee hotel.

I'VE GOT A SAVIOUR THAT'S MIGHTY TO KEEP

Tom Gibbons

In May 1956 'Duke' Tritton arranged an introduction between John Meredith and Ted Gibbons, licensee of the Centennial Hotel at Gulgong. Ted, one of the most co-operative helpers met by Meredith, deserves the thanks of everybody interested in the preservation of our native song. He himself played the piano accordion and the piano and always found time in the evening to slip away from the bar and sing a few songs in the back parlour.

Meredith booked in at the hotel for a weekend, having previously placed a notice in the local newspaper to say he was looking for traditional singers of bush songs. Permission to record and interview in the parlour was readily granted. Five performers attended, backed up by interested spectators.

First to be recorded was Teddy Gibbons' father, Tom, who was eighty-eight. He had lived all his life in Gulgong, earning his living as a brickmaker. He was proud of the fact that he had made the bricks for most of the township's existing buildings.

Bent over his walking stick as he sang, he took all his songs quietly, almost reverently, and only when reciting 'Alan Beyne' did he show real spirit.

THE MURDER OF ALAN BEYNE

They're taking me to the gallows, Mother,
They mean to hang me high;
They're going to gather round me,
And watch me as I die.
All earthly joys have vanished,
Now's gone each mortal hope,
They've drawn a cap across my eyes
And around my neck a rope.

The crazed mob will shout and groan,
And the priest will read a prayer,
The drop will fall from beneath my feet
And leave me in the air.
For they think I've murdered Alan Beyne,
For so the judge has said.
They'll hang me to the gallows, Mother,
They'll hang me till I'm dead.

Oh, the cattle drift beyond the orchard,
The last's on its way,
And the flowers that grow on the dear old garden
And the birds that sing and play
Are clear and pure of human blood,
And, Mother, so am I.
My father's grave on yonder hill
Its name without a stain;
I've ne'er had malice in my heart
Nor murdered Alan Beyne.

Yet twelve good men have found me guilty,
Or so the judge has said.
They'll hang me to the gallows, Mother,
They'll hang me till I'm dead.
Oh, the air is fresh and bracing, Mother,
The sun shines bright and high,
It is a pleasant day to live,
A gloomy one to die.

It is a bright and glorious day,
The joys of earth to grasp,
It is a sad and lonely one
To strangle, choke and gasp.

But let them doubt my lordly spirit
Or cow me if they can;
They send me like a rogue to death,
Yet I'll meet it like a man.

For I never murdered Alan Beyne,
But so the judge has said.
They'll hang me to the gallows, Mother,
They'll hang me till I'm dead.
Poor little sister Belle will weep,
And kiss me as I lie,
But kiss her twice or thrice for me
And tell her not to cry.

Tell her to weave a bright gay garment
And wear it as of yore,
Tell her to plant a lily on my grave
And think of me no more.
And tell that maiden whose love I sought
I was faithful yet;
But I must lie in a felon's grave
And she had best forget.

My memory's stained for ever,
Or so the judge has said.
They'll hang me to the gallows, Mother,
They'll hang me till I'm dead.
Lay me in my coffin, Mother,
As oft-times you have seen me rest,
One of my hands beneath my head,
And the other on my breast.

Place my Bible on my heart—
Nay, Mother, do not weep,
But kiss me as in the happier days
You kissed me when asleep.
And for the rest, it's far but right,
And little do I reek,
But cover up that cursed stain,
That black mark round my neck.

And pray for God's great blessing
On my devoted head,
For they'll hang me to the gallows, Mother,
They'll hang me till I'm dead.
Lay me not down by my father's side,
For once, I mind, he said
No child that stained his spotless name
Should share his mortal bed.

Old friends would look behind his grave
To my dishonoured one,
And my desserts would always serve
To hide his honoured one.
And I could fancy as there my corpse
And fettered limbs should lie
His growling skull and crumbling bones
Would mould and shrink from me away.

Yet I'll swear to God I'm innocent,
Never blood have I shed,
Yet they'll hang me to the gallows, Mother,
They'll hang me till I'm dead.
But hark! I hear a mighty murmur
Amongst the jostling crowd,
A cry, a shout, a roar of voices,
It echoed long and loud.

But see there dashes a horseman
On the folding scene, with tightly gathered rein;
He sits erect, he waves his hand—
Good heavens, it's Alan Beyne!
He waves his hand again and shouts,
The prisoner was reprieved,
Now, Mother, pray to the God you love
And raise your drooping head.
For all that's black and dark and grim
Are cheated of its dead.

The text of Tom Gibbons' version of 'Caledonio' is similar to
that of Joe Cashmere, but the tune is very different.

CALEDONIO

My name is Jimmy Randalls, in Glasgow I was born;
My home, my avocation, I was forced to leave in Scone.
For all the deeds that I have done I must now gang awoe
Far for to leave friends, hills and dales of Caledonio.

Very early one morning, just by the break of day,
I overheard a turnkey those cruel words to say:
'Arise, ye seven convicts. I warn ye, one and all,
This day you leave your once dear home of Caledonio.'

I slowly rose, put on my clothes, my heart was filled with grief;
My comrades standing round me could grant me no relief.
As I stepped into the morning coach my heart was filled with woe
Far for to leave friends, hills and dales of Caledonio.

Farewell, my loving sister, the only friend I have;
We kissed, embraced each other, as parting we shook hands.
Saying, 'I'll tell to you a sad tale when in a foreign land,
It was through a colonel's lady they sent me far awoe,
Far from those lovely hills and dales of Caledonio.'

Farewell, my ancient mother, I'm sorry for what I've done;
I hope there's no one casts down to you the horrid race I've run.
And may heavens above protect you when I am far awoe,
Far from those lovely hills and dales of Caledonio.

Farewell, my ancient father, you are the best of men;
Likewise my loving sweetheart, whose name was Catherine;
No more we'll roam together down by those clifty hills.
Then fare ye well, yon hills and dales of Caledonio.

We may not meet on earth again, we'll surely meet above,
Where hallelulia will be sang through all the strains of love;
There's but one judge and jury, it is Him who rules us all.
Then fare ye well, yon hills and dales of Caledonio.

'My Beautiful Muff' was always a great favourite with the drinkers in the back parlour at the Centennial. On winter's nights, Tom would sit there in front of the log fire, and sooner or later a request would be made for him to 'give lip to it'. Everybody joined in the chorus, 'My own and I'll wear it . . .'. Sometimes Teddy would sling the piano accordion around his neck and provide the accompaniment.

A handsome young damsel, one cold winter's night,
Away from her home she did happen to glide.
She was wrapped up very warmly with hair rather rough,
And in front she did wear a most beautiful muff.

CHORUS:
My own and I'll wear it,
(So) Don't you come near it;*
You'll spoil it, you'll tear it,
My beautiful muff.

Oh, she toddled on slowly away down the street,
Till a handsome young spark she did happen to meet.
He glided up slowly and said, sure enough,
'It's miss, you do wear a most beautiful muff.'

'Oh, my muff is the finest that ever you saw,
And all the young lads its attraction does draw.
It's lined with red velvet, and the outside is rough,
And as warm as a stole is my beautiful muff.

'Oh, my muff is my own, and it's nothing to you,
With me and my muff you have nothing to do;
It's a gift from Mama and it's elegant stuff,
And close to my jacket's my beautiful muff.'

* 'So' only occurs in some choruses.

Now the night being cold, she felt rather inclined
To go into a tap to have biscuits and wine,
Oh, the wine being strong she fell asleep fast enough,
And the lads they played hell with her beautiful muff.

Now when she awoke, she cried with surprise,
'My muff it is ruined for ever,' she cried.
'Oh, the lads they've got near it and played it queer tricks
And they've knocked out of shape my most beautiful muff.'

Now all you young girls who stroll out at night,
Be aware [sic] of the lads on whom you would light;
They'll booze you up quickly and that fast enough,
And tear a great hole in your beautiful muff.

Tom Gibbons' song of 'The Kelly Gang' has a tune similar to that used for 'Duke' Tritton's 'Goorianawa' (see p. 268).

THE KELLY GANG

Come, all young men with feeling!
With regret I must unfold,
I have a tale to tell of men
Whose hearts are stout and bold.

The odds against the Kelly gang
Were fifty if not more,
And yet there was not courage
For to face but only four.

Long life unto Kate Kelly,
For she was a noble girl;
She appeared upon the scene
In spite of all the world.

For true she loved her brothers,
Likewise the other two,
And so she proved to all the world
Her heart was fair and true.

If any praise be due at all,
Then let the praise be gave
To those four unfortunates
Who now lie in their graves.

Jim Gibbons

Tom's brother, Jim Gibbons, recited a ballad that seems to concern the race in which Alec Robertson was killed. Jim was an accomplished reciter of the bush kind. He became very excited when 'doing' the recitation 'How Tattersall's Cup Was Won', very much like a racing commentator, which, while adding dramatic appeal for the listeners, made the taking down of the words rather difficult.

HOW TATTERSALL'S CUP WAS WON

Fair, every heights are gleaming,
Beneath the sun God gave,
Great waves of life are swaying
Along the wheel-worn wave.
From cab and costly carriage,
From tram and creeping cart,
The sons of pain and pleasure
Pass in to play their part.

Old men who can remember
When first the Cup was run,
Sweet girls whose eyes are brighter
Than yonder flashing sun.
Proud dames whose cheeks are blushing
Although their blood be old,
Keen hawks whose hands are itching
To grasp each other's gold.

All mix and move and mangle,
All stand and ball and crush,
All beg and scream and battle
To find a winning horse.
While in the crowded paddocks,
The layers shout the odds,
And backers fling to trainers
And jockeys wait as gods.

One strikes, the curtain rises,
Young Fielder wins again;
Volcano's star has faded,
Hales rides him out in vain.
But now the backed green Egan
Runs home in front of all;
Once more the plungers tremble,
Once more the fielders fall.

The opening hacks are entered,
The layers' lips are still,
The heat and wheels are resting
On murmurs mighty mill [Mammon's mighty mill?].
Now the books re-open,
The wheels revolve once more,
And flushed with win and winnings
The backers regard their power.

At last the stand re-echoes
To the tramp of Herring's feet,
And trimming paddocks quiver
Like fields of wind-tossed wheat.
But now the stride of thunder
And Fielder soaring high,
And Robin Blood like splendour,
A high-bred field passed by.

Cross Fire has shunned the struggle,
Great Arsenal is gone,
Newcastle's erstwhile champion
Has left the gallant throng.
And Silvermine is saddled,
The Queen is fit and well,
And Chester's Handsome Daughter
Drifts like an equine belle.

At last the blazing summer
Strikes on the heated air,
The satin-coated champions
Their silk-clad riders bear.
And Daunton classes chargers,
And past the open gate
They glitter in waves of sunlight,
Walk slowly up the straight.

Fair womens' cheeks are lightened
As, turning, down they came [sic],
And up from lane and legging
Their floats of deep tone hung.
At length the field is marshalled,
All eyes are fixed on Keen,
His red flag falls like lightning,
And Oddward speeds The Queen.

With Uppercup she races;
Brave Endbolt's lying third,
But now the six-stone Drumstick
Goes past them like a bird
And, forcing all the running,
Leaves Fielder up the race
While close on Bowman's quarters
The waiting Acme lies.

Still from his horse's furlong,
The pony rounds the bend.
A cry goes up already,
He wins it end from end.
And onward down the running,
And past the heaving stand,
That all unknown outsider
Leads all that waiting band.

With The Queen's unboundless fire
That rank St Albans colt
Now leads the orange jacket,
While Acme and Ben Bolt
On Silvermine are closing;
And running strong and true
Behind the flying Squander
Sails mighty Dunedoo.

But now the pace grows hotter,
The blue and black comes back,
And Cornwall's white and scarlet
Is leading Cooper's Track.
But Donald holds Less Fire,
Bare half a length away
And rounding Cutter's corner
The featherweights made play.

At Oxman's, young Fielder
Runs up the Drumstick's side,
But answering the challenge
Again he deeps the tide.
Hard Gale is bringing Bowman,
And Rouse's colours shine,
Besides The Drummer's Daughter
And clear on Silvermine.

Tom Hales sits still on Acme,
And waiting on the rails,
While Gorge on Dark Invader
Still hangs upon their tails.
But now the white and orange
Beats Drumstick by a neck
With Uppercut's nostrils
The foam flies fleck on fleck.

He fails, and Gorge and Donald
Take up the desperate chase,
While Silvermine and Ben Bolt
Each stride increase their pace.
For close behind them thunders
A field that sways and strains,
Each silk and skin all dotted
And dotted with crimson stains.

They reach the last three furlongs,
All fighting for the place,
Their risen colours mangle
As knee to knee they race.
I see their sick white faces,
I hear the ring-spear speak.
Great God! Three men are lying
Beneath the cruel feet.

Gone is the swift Best Fire
From out that battling band,
Great Silvermine has fallen,
Downtrodden are horse and man.
Above them lies Invader,
And o'er the cruel mass
On hooves that crush and batter
As maddened horses pass.

From out the dust and flashing
Which steed and satin flows,
And o'er the fallen horsemen
The scattered field swept close.
No time have men to study
When spurs are wet and red,
So onward raced the living
And trampled lie the dead.

The Drumstick stays and peppers,
While past him Bowman sails;
Stout Dunedoo is reeling,
The Drummer's Daughter fails;
She overreached the distance.
Each shorten in their stride,
While Hales is lifting Acme
To Bowman's bloody side.

Loud from the stand is reeling,
That in the turn proclaim,
The colt and mare surge homeward,
Their nostrils all aflame.
But now the child of Chester
Comes to the victor's calls,
And Bowman nobly answers
Each stinging cut that falls.

Mid shouts, big heels to Bowman
The colt regains his lead,
While whips and spurs are sliding
On sides that even bleed.
Still on the sway and struggle
Again the two are wed,
Till 'neath the box's shadows
Hales wins by half a head.

Jim Gibbons also knew a few toasts. One he explained by say-ing, 'When Molly Campbell, the barmaid, was shoutin' for any-one that could give the best toast, at Coonamble Hotel, a man come in and he said:

> *'My name is Jimmy Gamble,*
> *From pub to pub I ramble.*
> *If that don't do,*
> *Well, strike me blue!*
> *I'll kiss you, Molly Campbell.'*

This was presumably the winning toast, and, as it was not

particularly funny or noteworthy, John Meredith thought Jim Gibbons would be the only person to remember it. Yet some time later, when drinking in the local pub at Thirlmere, a village on the Picton-Mittagong loopline, John and the other patrons of the bar were bailed up by a belligerent drunk. Everyone gave him a wide berth and he had half of the room to himself. He bawled out what sounded like snatches of bush ballads, and then suddenly—

> *If that won't do,*
> *Well, strike me blue!*
> *You can call me Mother Campbell.*

He sounded like a possible source of songs, but while John was considering whether it was advisable to try and talk to him, he collapsed in a stupor.

During another visit to Thirlmere, Meredith was in luck and met the old chap about six middies earlier in his drinking. He was rather suspicious and not inclined to perform, but he did recite the verse a few times. He had never been to Coonamble, but learned the ditty 'somewhere during the war'.

> *I'm Paddy the rake,*
> *Make no mistake,*
> *From pub to pub I ramble.*
> *I'm Paddy the dog,*
> *I'm Paddy the sod,*
> *I drink and swear and gamble.*
> *If that won't do,*
> *Well, strike me blue!*
> *And call me Mother Campbell.*

One set of verses with a touch of bush flavour recited by Jim Gibbons brought up again the view of Victorians as notorious scabs.

CLANCY'S PRAYER

> *Whilst on the track, away outback,*
> *A night I camped with Clancy.*
> *When going to bed, his prayers he said,*
> *But this one took my fancy.*
>
> *'Oh Lord,' said he, 'I pray to thee,*
> *While misery round us rages,*
> *May bad luck fall on one and all*
> *Who tries to cut down wages.*

254

'May the devil pursue that labour brew,
And to hell I wish he'd take it.
When men come seek ten bob a week
A very hot job they'll make it.

'May conscience sting old Whitley King,
And frown him to damnation.
May all white wings spread deep their wants [sic],
In misery and starvation.

'When union men to seek a pen
To Noo South Wales come steerin',
They'll take a job at fifteen bob,
Lamb-markin' until shearin'.

'Such men as them, I say,
Disgrace the name of union.
Each one I'd kick back into Vic.,
For Noo South Wales they're ruinin'.'

Mrs Mason

The notice which, as mentioned before, John Meredith placed in the Gulgong newspaper was seen by a Mrs Mason who lived some distance from the town. After reading the paragraph she made a trip to the township to lilt the tune she knew for 'The Wild Colonial Boy'. Meredith succeeded in getting the air on tape, but then, while he was preparing for further recording in the crowded room, Mrs Mason slipped away before details of the source of the tune could be obtained.

THE WILD COLONIAL BOY

Bill Coughlin

Bill Coughlin walked into the Centennial Hotel during John Meredith's first visit to Gulgong and announced that he knew a song. It was about shearing, he said, and probably would not be of any use. No time was lost in getting him before the microphone, but his nervousness brought on an asthma attack and the recording was not successful. A couple of glasses of stout made him feel more at ease, so another, more fruitful, attempt was made.

THE UNION BOY

When first I arrived in Quirindi, those girls they jumped with joy,
Saying one unto the other, 'Here comes a union boy.

'We'll treat him to a bottle, and likewise to a dram;
Our hearts we'll fairly give, too, to all staunch union men.'

I had not long been in Quirindi, not one week, two or three,
When a handsome, pretty, fair maid, she fell in love with me.

She introduced me to her mother as a loyal union man,
'Oh, mother, dearest mother, now he's gently joined that gang.'

'Oh, daughter, dearest daughter, oh, this never can be,
For four years ago-oh, he scabbed it at Forquadee.'

'Oh, mother, dearest mother, now the truth to you I'll tell,
He's since then joined the union and the country knows it well.

'Now, Fred, you've joined the union, so stick to it like glue,
For the scabs that were upon your back they're now but only few.

'And if ever you go black-leggin' or scabbing likewise,
It's with my long, long fingernails I'll scratch out both your eyes.

'I'll put you to every cruelty, I'll stretch you in a vice,
I'll cut you up in a hay machine and sell you for Chinee rice.

[Line missing]
And down in Quirindi Creek, your body I will throw.'

256

Come, all you young and old men, oh, wherever you may be,
Oh, it's hoist-oh the flag-oh, the flag of unity.

Then scabbin' in this 'counteree' will soon be at an end,
And I pray that one and all of you will be staunch union men.

Coughlin was seventy when recorded, but had learned 'The Union Boy' at Cassilis during a shearers' strike in 1902. He was only sixteen years of age at that time.

Folk Songs of Canada includes a song, 'Ye Maids of Ontario', to a tune closely resembling Coughlin's and three verses of the text are almost identical with lines from 'The Union Boy', except that the place is Quebec Town and the loyal union boy is a roving shanty-man. Other lines in the Canadian song are stated to occur in the Irish song, 'The Roving Journeyman', and 'The Roving Gambler' of North America.

A variant of Coughlin's tune appears as the melodic basis of 'Johnny Harte', a ballad about a young girl's love for a soldier boy beneath her in social rank, in Colm O Lochlainn's *Irish Street Ballads*.

An even earlier memory of Coughlin's, not quite complete, was 'Boston City', which is well known in both England and the United States under various titles. Coughlin learned this at Uarbry, New South Wales, when he was eight, which probably accounts for the fact he could no longer recall all the words.

BOSTON CITY

I was born in Boston City, boys, in a place you all know well,
Brought up by honest parents and the truth to you I'll tell;
Brought up by honest parents and reared most tenderly,
Till I became a roving lad at the age of twenty-three.

R

My character it was taken and I was sent to jail;
Although my friends they tried to bail me out, but it was of no avail.
[2 lines missing]

To see my poor old father, while standing at the bar,
Also my aged mother with the tearing of her hair;
A-tearing at her old grey locks, as the tears came trinkling down,
Saying, 'Son, dear son, what have you done to be sent to Noo York
   town?'

They put me on an east-bound train one dark and stormy night,
[Start of line missing] *to hear them say.*
'There goes that mounted burgular, in iron chains he's bound;
For the robbery of the Boston Bank he's bound for Noo York town.'

If ever I gain my liberty [line incomplete]
I'll give up drinking and gambling, and also-wise the rum.
I'll—

 'That's all I know of it. . . .'
 This old chap did much better in remembering another of
those sentimental ballads of World War I, 'On the Banks of the
Murray'. Alan Scott has also collected this in the Wollongong
district.

ON THE BANKS OF THE MURRAY

In a neat little cot on the banks of the Murray
Lived the wife of a family with children so poor.
Oh, what a scene when he kissed his poor mother,
The last one he kissed in this cruel cold world.

He whispered a touching goodbye to his mother,
His country was calling, his flag was unfold [sic];
Those were the words that were uttered when parting,
Goodbye, my mother, and Goodbye, my son.

It's—Kiss little Daisy, my dear little daughter,
And say I'll return when the battle is won.

The transport led on to the scene of the slaughter,
And landed our boys in the thick of the fray.
Our hero was shot at the Dardanelles battle,
Lay mortally wounded and dying this day.

It's—Give this watch to my own darling mother,
This locket and chain to my dear little daughter,
And the rest you may give to my dear wife and brother,
For God has denied me to see them again.

Oh, what a change in that neat little cottage!
A mother sits rocking a baby just born,
While the poor aged mother sits rocking and moaning,
For the son she loves dearly will never return.

While poor little Daisy keeps asking for poppa,
The mother replies, though her poor heart's near breaking,
Your father, my darling, was shot at the war.

John Meredith made several attempts to get all the words of
'The Springtime It Brings On the Shearing' from Bill Coughlin,
but he could only recall one or two verses and odd, mixed-up
lines.

THE SPRINGTIME IT BRINGS ON THE SHEARING

You talk of those Sydney flash mashers,
And the flashest of fellers in town,
There's nothing more flasher than shearers
When shearin', when shearin' comes round.
But they talk and walk in their sleep,
And they talk and walk in their sleep,
And they growl at the cook and his tucker,
And snore in their sleep . . .
There's nothing more flasher than shearers,
When shearin', when shearin' comes round.
And soon you'll find those flash shearers
Makin' johnny-cakes down in the bend.
There's nothing more flasher than shearers
When shearin', when shearin' comes round.

Tom Tattersall

The two songs sung by Tom Tattersall sound as though they
originated in North America and possibly both were an inheri-
tance left by Californians at the Gulgong goldfields. Tattersall's
melodious tenor voice made the songs really pleasant listening.

ON THE BANKS OF THE OLD OMAHA

I will sing you a song of sweet Julia,
And she lived far beneath the western star.
I never shall forget the first time we met
On the banks of the old Omaha.

CHORUS:

> *On the banks of the old Omaha,*
> *Where we've spent together many years,*
> *Where the wild birds flutter and sing among the trees,*
> *On the banks of the old Omaha.*

Sweet Julia she said, 'I'm going,'
When there came a knocking at the door,
And that very same night sweet Julia she died
On the banks of the old Omaha.

Sweet Julia she now lies a-sleeping
In her grave far beneath the western star,
And my heart it is there in that valley so fair
On the banks of the old Omaha.

THE LITTLE ROSEWOOD CASKET

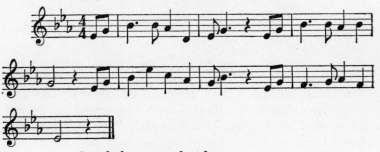

> *In a little rosewood casket*
> *That is resting on a stand*
> *There's a package of old letters*
> *Written by my true love's hand.*

> *Go and get them now, dear sister,*
> *And read them all tonight,*
> *For I've often tried, but I could not,*
> *For my tears would blind my sight.*

> *Read those precious lines so slowly*
> *That I'll not miss even one,*
> *And the precious hand that wrote them*
> *His last words for me is done.*

Go and tell him I never blamed him
Not a unkind word was spoke,
Will you tell him, sister, tell him
That my heart in coldness broke.

When I'm dead and in my coffin,
And the crowd around me bound,
And the little bed is ready
In the cold and silent ground,

Place his letters and his locket
Both together on my heart,
And the little ring he gave me
From my finger never part.

You have finished now, dear sister.
Will you read them all again?
While I listen to you read them
I will lose all sense of pain.

While I listen to you read them
I will gently fall asleep,
And a little walk with Jesus,
Oh, dear sister, do not weep.

Herb Tattersall

Herb is the brother of Tom Tattersall and learned 'Old Dan Tucker' from their father. He said there were several more verses that escaped his memory. This chap played the concertina and several kinds of zither. The zither he liked best of all was called a 'guitar-banjo-mandolin' and was akin to a zither strung with strings in pairs like a mandolin. When it was played, the effect was like a carillon of small bells.

The tune of 'Old Dan Tucker' was well known in Gulgong district. It was played on the accordion, as 'Oh, Dear Mother, What a Fool I've Been', by both Tom Blackman junior and another bush musician called Charlie Bennett, who, though now living in Sydney, spent his early life in the Gulgong area. Also, one of the Four Sisters ensemble of Sydney played it as a step-dance, but under the remarkable name of 'The Black Man Piddled in the White Man's Shoe'.

262

OLD DAN TUCKER

Old Danny Tucker was a dirty old man,
He washed his face in the frying pan,
Combed his hair with the leg of a chair,
Died with a toothache in his hair.

Herb Tattersall had a liking for setting verse to tunes he knew and sang 'Oh, Bedad Then, Says I' and 'Stringybark' to the same music.

OH, BEDAD THEN, SAYS I

You asked me to sing you a bit of a song,
Well, it's not very short nor it's not very long;
You asked me to sing you a something that's new—
Well, bedad then, says I, I don't care if I do.

Well, me name is Dan Murphy, a farmer am I,
I courted a lass and I felt rather shy;
She bid me come in for a moment or two—
Well, bedad then, says I, I don't care if I do.

Well, we entered the kitchen—'twas cosy and bright;
A fine, hearty supper I put out of sight.
Said she, Here's a drop of the old mountain dew—
Well, bedad then, says I, I don't care if I do.

Now, when I was finished, I picked up me hat;
Says Peggy, Me darlin', don't leave me like that.
She asked me to kiss her like fond lovers do—
Well, bedad then, says I, I don't care if I do.

Then we kissed and we squeezed and to lover's delight;
She asked me to wed her and make her my wife.
Says she, I've a cow and an acre or two—
Well, bedad then, says I, I don't care if I do.

In was early next morning to the church to get wed;
The priest stood and faced us with a book, and he said,
Now, let you take Peggy and Peggy take you—
Well, bedad then, says I, I don't care if I do.

'Stringybark' was a piece of verse Herb learned from some-one when he was still attending school.

STRINGYBARK
There are white-box and pine on the ridges afar,
Where the ironbark, bluegum and peppermint are;
But the one I know best and the dearest to me
And the king of them all is the stringybark tree.

Now, from stringybark slabs were the walls of the hut,
From stringybark saplings the rafters were cut,
And the roof that long sheltered my brothers and me
Were the broad sheets of bark from the stringybark tree.

Authorship of 'The Dying Sleeper-cutter', or 'Cant-hook and Wedges', is doubtful. Norman Rowland said he made it up in 1932 during the depression, when only a lad of fourteen. Herb Tattersall denied this, claiming that, although Rowland began the composition, he never quite finished it off. The general consensus of opinion was that the song was a joint effort. Yet neither of the men could sing the complete song! Their two versions together cover roughly four verses and a chorus. The tune used was that for the version of 'The Dying Stockman' on p. 226.

CANT-HOOK AND WEDGES
An old sleeper-cutter lay dying
With a broad-axe supporting his head.
All around him the others were standing,
When he raised on his pillow and said:

'*Wrap me up with my cant-hook and wedges,*
And bury me deep down below,
Down where the tall-cogs can't haunt me,
Where the five-cut wavy-grains grow.'

'*There's no teeth in the buckled old cross-saw,*
No stern in the splintered old mall,
And I bet my hobnails there isn't
No rum in the billy at all.

'*And the T-model's bogged in a gully,*
No shovel to put her on top,
[2 lines missing]

'*It's goodbye to the cutting on Dennis,*
Goodbye to Sunday Flat, too,
Goodiman's I cut out and finished,
And I am saying sad farewell to you.'

Norm Rowland's version was as follows:

Wrap me up in my cant-hooks and wedges,
And bury me deep down below,
Down where the tall-toms can't haunt me,
Down where the five-cut wavy-grains grow.

We was cutting back on Denny's,
In nineteen forty-two,
We hadn't prog in the camp at the time,
We called it Calico Town.

And Fred Lyons was the carter, too,
And the old Ford was bogged down to the axle,
Down in the goo,
But we packed it and come out too.

And Danny MacGrath's timber
Was the goodest we could see. . . .
[or, '*Was as good as we could see*']

Gladys Scrivener's version of 'Rock All Our Babies'—she called it 'Rock-a-bye Baby'—has not been included in this book, but it may be mentioned here that the words she used were only slightly different from those of Herb Tattersall and that her tune was virtually the same; she used a lullaby chorus as an addition to each verse.

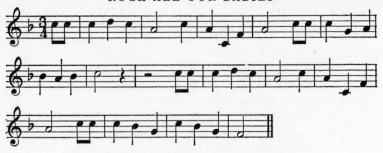

Oh, show me the lady that never would roam
Away from her fireside at night,
And never go roaming out after the boys,
But sit by her fireside so bright.

My wife she's one of a different kind,
Often caused me a lot of grief;
She's off from her home, she leaves me alone
To rock all our babies to sleep.

I remember one night when I came back home
I came in as quiet as a lamb;
She must have had company for when I walked in
I heard the back door when it slammed.

I walked right in and looked all around,
I never thought that she would cheat;
Without a doubt, she'd just gone out,
And left all our babies to sleep.

Just the other night while out for a walk
I happened to stroll down the street,
And to my surprise, I saw with my eyes,
My wife with a man off the street.

She said, 'It's no harm, so please don't alarm,
To make any fuss on the street.'
She tickled my chin and ordered me in
To rock all our babies to sleep.

'Cat' McManus

In June 1959 the Bush Music Club gave a concert at Gulgong
to assist the appeal for funds to build new swimming baths. The
Club's members were billeted at Enid McKenzie's Royal Hotel,

and after the concert their hostess put on a small supper party in the dining-room.

It was a memorable musical evening with all the local singers taking turns to perform. John Meredith says reminiscently that it was almost Henry's Lawson's 'The Songs They Used To Sing' lived over again—even to the low-ceilinged room with a wide, open fireplace—and that he at least would not have been surprised if Henry had walked in and joined the mob.

Between the items there were repeated requests for 'Cat' McManus to sing 'The Maiden's Prayer'. Only a young man, 'Cat' was reluctant to do so, not because of shyness, but because the mate from whom he had learned the song had shortly before been killed in an accident. The source was Alan ('Killer') Riley, a truck-driver, who had picked it up from a tent-mate while trapping rabbits in the Bourke district.

THE MAIDEN'S PRAYER

A maiden young and fair was she,
Who lived in high society.
A soldier brave and bold was he,
Who stole of her virginity.

And when her apron strings hung low
He chased her through the ice and snow.
And now her apron strings don't meet
He passes her by in the street.

Her father, returning late one night,
He found her home without a light.
He went straightway up to her room
And found her hanging in the gloom.

[2 lines missing]
He took a knife and cut her down,
And on her breast these words he found:

267

Oh, Father, Father, dig my grave,
Place me beside a garden wall,
And on my grave place a turtle-dove
To show this world I died for love.

'Duke' Tritton

'The Duke', who was in his late seventies when he died in 1965, spent most of his life knocking about the bush working at almost every occupation possible to a man—he was shearer, fencer, goldminer, professional boxer, carrier, and farmer. He had, of course, humped the bluey many times. The story of this remarkable man's early life is told in his *Time Means Tucker*, first published by the *Bulletin* in 1959. When John Meredith met him, Tritton lived at Cullenbone, between Mudgee and Gulgong.

'Goorianawa' he learned from an uncle staying with his family at Belmore between shearing seasons. This was when 'Duke' was eight or nine years old.

GOORIANAWA

I've been many years a shearer, and fancied I could shear,
I've shore for Rouse of Guntawang and always missed the spear;
I've shore for Nicholas Bayly, and I declare to you
That on his pure Merinos I could always struggle through.

CHORUS:
> *But, oh my! I never saw before*
> *The way we had to knuckle down at Goorianawa.*

I've been shearing down the Bogan, as far as Dandaloo,
For good old Reid of Tabratong I've often cut a few;
Haddon Rig and Quambone, and even Wingadee—
I could close my shears at six o'clock with a quiet century.

I've been shearing on the Goulburn side and down at Douglas Park,
Where every day 'twas 'Wool away!' and Toby did his work.
I've shore for General Stewart, whose tomb is on 'The Mount',
And the sprees I've had with Scrammy Jack are more than I can count.

I've shore for John McMaster down on Rockedgial Creek,
And I could always dish him up with thirty score a week.
I've shore at Terramungamine and on the Talbragar,
And I ran McDermott for the cobbler when we shore at Buckingbar.

I've been shearing at Eugowra—I'll never forget the name,
Where Gardiner robbed the escort that from the Lachlan came.
I've shore for Bob Fitzgerald down at the Dabee Rocks,
McPhillamy of Charlton and Mister Henry Cox.

That was in the good old days—you might have heard them say
How Skellycorn from Bathurst rode to Sydney in a day.
But now I'm broken-mouthed and my shearing's at an end,
And though they called me 'Whalebone' I was never known to bend.

LAST CHORUS:
 But, spare me flamin' days! I never saw before
 The way we had to knuckle down at Goorianawa.

'Duke' knew a great many songs and fragments of songs, but
could not remember where he learned most of them. He also
wrote several songs in the style of the traditional Australian
ballad. He said that in the outback Lawson was sung almost as
much as he was recited, possibly because so much of his verse
was written in ballad metre and so fitted easily to traditional
tunes.

BALLAD OF THE DROVER

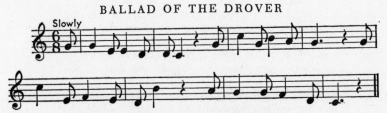

Across the stony ridges, across the rolling plain,
Young Harry Dale, the drover, is riding home again.
How well his stock-horse bears him, and light of heart is he,
And stoutly his old packhorse is trotting by his knee.

[2 lines missing]
He hums a song of someone he hopes to marry soon;
While hobble-chains and camp-ware are jingling to the tune.

'Well, that's just about chopped me on that,' he commented as he ran out of text.

Another Lawson poem sung by 'Duke' Tritton was the bushranging ballad 'Taking His Chance', which was learned from Emily Babbage of Mudgee about 1906.

TAKING HIS CHANCE

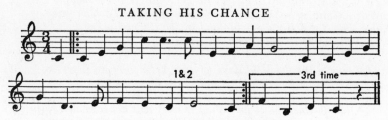

They stood by the door of the Inn on the Rise;
May Carney looked up in the bushranger's eyes:
'Oh! why did you come?—it was mad of you, Jack;
You know that the troopers are out on your track.'
A laugh and a shake of his obstinate head—
'I wanted a dance, and I'll chance it,' he said.

Some twenty-odd bushmen had come to the ball,
But Jack from his youth had been known to them all,
And bushmen are soft where a woman is fair,
So the love of May Carney protected him there.
Through all the short evening—it seems like romance—
She danced with a bushranger taking his chance.

'Twas midnight—the dancers stood suddenly still,
For hoof-beats were heard on the side of the hill!
Ben Duggan, the drover, along the hillside
Came riding as only a bushman can ride.
He sprang from his horse, to the dancers he sped—
'The troopers are down in the gully!' he said.

Quite close to the shanty the troopers were seen.
'Clear out and ride hard for the ranges, Jack Dean!
Be quick!' said May Carney—her hand on her heart—
'We'll bluff them awhile and 'twill give you a start.'
He lingered a moment—to kiss her, of course—
Then ran to the trees where he'd hobbled his horse.

She ran to the gate, and the troopers were there—
The jingle of hobbles came faint on the air—
Then loudly she screamed: it was only to drown
The treacherous clatter of sliprails let down.
But troopers are sharp, and she saw at a glance
That someone was taking a desperate chance.

They chased and they shouted 'Surrender, Jack Dean!'
They called him three times in the name of the Queen.
Then came from the darkness the clicking of locks;
The crack of a rifle was heard in the rocks!
A shriek, and a shout, and a rush of pale men—
And there lay the bushranger, chancing it then.

The sergeant dismounted and knelt on the sod—
'Your bushranging's over—make peace, Jack, with God!'
The dying man laughed—not a word he replied,
But turned to the girl who knelt down by his side.
He gazed in her eyes as she lifted his head:
'Just kiss me, my girl, and I'll chance it,' he said.

In the late nineties, when busking around Sydney's streets with Danny Clements, 'Duke', then just into his teens, learned 'The Shores of Botany Bay'. He said he had heard 'The Shores of Americay' sung to the same tune.

THE SHORES OF BOTANY BAY

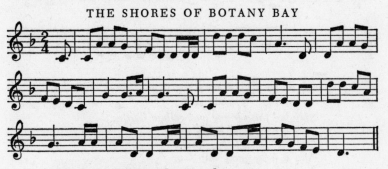

Oh, I'm on my way down to the quay,
Where a big ship now does lay,
For to take a gang of navvies
I was told to engage;
But I thought I would call in for a while
Before I went away,
For to take a trip in an emigrant ship
To the shores of Botany Bay.

> *Farewell to your bricks and mortar,*
> *Farewell to your dirty lime,*
> *Farewell to your gangway hand-gang planks,*
> *And to hell with your overtime!*
> *For the good ship* Rag o' Muffin
> *Is a-lying at the quay,*
> *For to take old Pat with a shovel on his back*
> *To the shores of Botany Bay.*

> *For the boss came up this morning,*
> *And he said, 'Well, Pat, hello!*
> *If you do not mix that mortar fast*
> *Be sure you'll have to go.'*
> *Of course, he did insult me,*
> *I demanded all my pay,*
> *And I told him straight I was going to emigrate*
> *To the shores of Botany Bay.*

Tritton's memory failed him after two verses of 'Ten Thousand Miles Away'. 'Well,' he said, 'that's all I remember of that, unfortunately.'

TEN THOUSAND MILES AWAY

> *Sing ho! for a brave and gallant barque*
> *And a brisk and lively crew,*
> *Sing ho! for a jolly captain*
> *And a jolly good ship too.*
> *To carry me over the sea, my boys,*
> *To my true love away.*
> *For she's taken a trip in a government ship*
> *Ten thousand miles away.*

> *Oh, my true love was handsome,*
> *And my true love was young,*
> *Her eyes were blue as the violets hue*
> *And silvery sounds her tongue.*

And silvery sounds her tongue, my boys,
And while I sing this lay,
She's a-doing the grand in a distant land
Ten thousand miles away.

When working on a fencing contract on Gumin station in the Warrumbungle Range area, 'Duke' Tritton met Jack Large of Mudgee, an uncle of the Fred Large of Ulan already mentioned in this book. Jack taught him the song 'The Great Northern Line', but over the years Tritton slowly forgot parts of it. Recently, when he met two old cronies from Coonabarabran, Billy Conn and Billy Harlow, an ex-bullocky, 'Duke' mentioned the song. Between them all they recalled old Jack Large's version and later Tritton recorded it for John Meredith.

The tune is much the same as the one to which Sally Sloane sings 'The Knickerbocker Line' (see p. 195).

THE GREAT NORTHERN LINE

My love he is a teamster, a handsome man is he,
Red shirt, white moleskin trousers, and hat of cabbage-tree;
He drives a team of bullocks, and whether it's wet or fine
You will hear his whip a-cracking on the Great Northern Line.

CHORUS:
    Watch him, pipe him, twig him how he goes,
    With his little team of bullocks, he cuts no dirty shows;
    He's one of the flash young carriers that on the road do shine,
    With his little team of bullocks on the Great Northern Line.

And when he swings the greenhide whip he raises skin and hair;
His bullocks all have shrivelled horns, for, Lordy, he can swear!
But I will always love him, this splendid man of mine,
With his little team of bullocks on the Great Northern Line.

When he bogged at Mundowie and the bullocks took the yoke,
They strained with bellies on the ground until the bar-chain broke.
He fixed it up with fencing wire and brought wool from Bundamine,
With his little team of bullocks on the Great Northern Line.

When he comes into Tamworth you will hear the ladies sigh,
And parents guard their daughters, for he has a roving eye;
But he signals with his bullock-whip as he comes through the pine,
With his little team of bullocks on the Great Northern Line.

273

S

Tritton claimed that 'Banjo' Paterson actually wrote the music-hall type satire on 'The War Correspondent'. 'Having a crack at himself,' Duke said, but this is extremely doubtful, although Paterson was a war correspondent during the Boer War.

THE WAR CORRESPONDENT

You'll all have heard of 'Banjo' Paterson and of course I needn't say
That he's the latest and the greatest correspondent of the day.
And now you have the privilege of gazing on the elf;
I represent the pippers, and the papers and myself.

I know a lot of editors and creditors and such [? subs],
Publishers and polishers and perishers and pubs,
Novelists and obelisks and parliamentary daddies,
Somersaults and lunatics and other tooraladdies.

What I've gone through none will ever, ever know;
You'll find out when you go to heaven, so,
Rule Britannia, De Rougemont's out of the hunt.
There's no one bred like a thoroughbred journalist,
They're hot stuff and I'm the infernalest,
That's me, I'm he, the war correspondent of the front.

Tritton sang fragments of two shearing songs. 'Shearing at Castlereagh' was to a variant of the tune he used for 'Cobb and Co.' (not included here).

SHEARING AT CASTLEREAGH

The bells are set a-ringing and the engine gives a toot,
There are five and thirty shearers here a-shearing for the loot.
So stir yourselves, you penners-up, what would the buyers say
In London if the wool was late this year from Castlereagh!

The man that keeps the cutters sharp is growling in his cage,
He's always in a hurry and he's always in a rage.
'You clumsy-fisted mutton-heads, you'd make a feller sick!
You class yourselves as shearers, but you were born to swing a pick.'

Bob McCormack of Mudgee told Tritton that 'Good for a Rush or a Rally' was originally written about Jack Howe, the big-gun shearer. 'Duke' could not remember where he first heard it, but depending upon McCormack's recollection of the song's content he wrote a new set of verses using the four lines he did remember as a chorus.

The song 'The Irishman's Gold Mine', which Tritton learned 'somewhere in the north-west' when he was a young man, was sung to a variant of the tune used in 'Rock All Our Babies' by

275

Herb Tattersall, 'Where's Your Licence?' by Gladys Scrivener, and 'The Reedy Lagoon'.

GOOD FOR A RUSH OR A RALLY

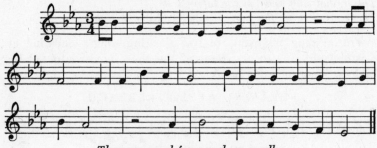

They are good for a rush or a rally,
But they have no bottom to stay,
But when I go out for a tally,
I shear two hundred a day.

THE IRISHMAN'S GOLDMINE

'Twas a long time ago, just how long I don't know,
Since I first saw the land of the gumtree.
I was young, I was bold, I was looking for gold,
I was gay as the bloom of the plum-tree.

So it was pleasing to me when I happened to see
An Italian named Paddy O'Higgins,
For by him I was told, if I want to find gold,
I must hump my swag up to the diggings.

So I bid him good-day and I went on my way
With my heart twice as light as a feather,

276

And I whistle and sing till the gumtrees they ring,
And I don't give a damn for the weather.

So I walks me all day till I gets me that way
That I cannot stand up without sittin',
For the weight of my pack puts a kink in my back
That I cannot get out without splittin'.

I was ready to cry when I happened to spy
A red shirt with a big man inside it.
When my tale him I told, and I spoke about gold,
He said, 'Irish, you're sitting beside it!

'See that big yellow lump, there beside the black stump—
If you want to find gold I'd advise you
Dig it up, and I bet you won't ever forget,
For what you'll find there will surprise you.'

So I bid him good-day and he goes on his way,
And that hump, I just felt I could hug it;
For my heart was so big as I started to dig
And expected to find one big nugget.

I can see myself now, with the sweat on my brow,
As off that big hump I then flung me,
For those great soldier-ants they climbed up my pants
And like ten thousand deevils they stung me.

How they climbed in and out, picking little bits out,
Like goats that were turned into clover.
How I wished I was home, never more would I roam,
How I cursed the gold over and over.

How they stung and they hurt as I pulled off my shirt,
How I cursed that damn Paddy O'Higgins!
How I wished that red shirt, as I rolled in the dirt,
Had been buried alive in the diggings.

Now, I remember one day that I heard the priest say
That gold was the root of all evil.
It was true what he told, for I went to find gold
And dug up the roots of the deevil.

Thomas Bleakley

In a letter to Nancy Keesing, which she generously passed on
to John Meredith, Thomas Bleakley wrote of two songs he
remembered.

'Sixty years ago, when I was a lad of fifteen years, I lived for a time with a country postmaster, who had spent some years of service in the far west of Queensland. From him I learned several songs, which he sang well, but his favourites were the Neumerella Shore and another, The Place Where the Old Horse Died.'

Mr Bleakley recorded the songs for Alan Scott in 1955, when he was seventy-six years of age.

THE NEUMERELLA SHORE

There's a long green gully on the Neumerella shore
Where I've 'longed though many is the day;
All by my selection I have acres by the score,
So I'll unyoke my bullocks from the dray.

    To my cattle I do say, you may feed, feed away,
    But you'll never be impounded any more,
    For you're running, running, running on the duffer's piece of land,
    Free-selected on the Neumerella shore.

When the moon is shining bright and has climbed the mountains high,
We will saddle up our horses and away.
We will steal the squatter's cattle by the darkness of the night,
And we'll brand at the dawn of the day.

And now, my pretty calf, at the squatter you may laugh,
But you'll never see your owner any more,
For you're running, running, running on the duffer's piece of land,
Free-selected on the Neumerella shore.

And when we get the swag we'll steal the squatter's nag,
And we'll sell him in some distant inland town;
And when we get the cash, oh, we chaps will cut a dash,
For the doing of the squatter so brown.

To John Robertson we say, you've been leading us astray,
And we never can believe you any more;
For we chaps can get a livin' far easier by thievin'
Than by farming on the Neumerella shore.

'These two old songs,' Mr Bleakley continued, 'I have never forgotten, and I frequently sang them, both at home and at parties, to my own vamped accompaniment. I have never heard these songs sung by anyone else since, and have no idea of their origin.'

THE PLACE WHERE THE OLD HORSE DIED

In the hollow by the pollard, where the crop is tall and rank,
Of the dockweed and the nettle growing free,
Where the bramble and the brushwood climb unheeded o'er the bank,
And the pigat jerks and chatters on the trees,

There's a spot I never pass in the brushwood and the grass
But for very shame I turn my head aside,
While the tears fall thick and hot, and my curse is on the spot,
'Tis the place where the old horse died.

Was he blown? I do not think it. Did he slip? I cannot tell.
We had run for forty minutes in the vale;
He was reaching at his bridle, he was going strong and well,
And he never seemed to falter or to fail.
Though I sometimes fancy, too, that his daring spirit knew
The task beyond the compass of his stride,
Yet he faced it true and brave and he jumped into his grave
At the place where the old horse died.

I was up in half a minute but he never seemed to stir,
Though I scored him with my rowels in the fall.
In his life he'd never felt before the insult of the spurs,
Then I knew that it was over once for all,
As motionless he lay on his cheerless bed of clay,
Huddled up without a murmur on his side;
'Twas a hard and bitter stroke, for his honest back was broke,
At the place where the old horse died.

There are men both good and wise who hold that in the future state
Dumb creatures we have cherished here below
Shall give us joyous greeting as we pass the Golden Gate—
Is it folly if I hope it may be so?
For never man had friend more enduring to the end,
More faithful, what the turn of life and tide;
Oh, the memory gives me pain. I shall never ride again
O'er the place where the old horse died.

A retired cattleman and drover, Mr W. R. Chisholm of Charters Towers, Queensland, forwarded some notes on 'The Place Where the Old Horse Died' to Meredith:

'. . . I am nearly certain this is an English song. I haven't heard it for fifty years and the man who sang it was a raw Pommy who hadn't been out here long enough to have picked up much of our songs or folklore. He sang two other songs at the same sing-song which were definitely English. One was The Midship Mite, a rollicking sea-tale, but mournful, and the other was In the Gloaming, a love song. He had a good voice for a bush camp and was called on to sing again. Later, I spent some months in his company digging out poison bush, just the two of us, so I often heard him sing again on quiet nights with the dingoes joining in the chorus.'

The couple of verses of 'The Place Where the Old Horse Died'
recalled by Mr Chisholm were as follows:

There's a pocket in the hedgerows where the grass is tall and rank,
With the dog-wood and the nettle growing free,
Where the bramble and the brushwood straggle blindly o'er the bank,
With the foxglove and the myrtle on the lea.

Through the sedges and the grass, there's a spot I never pass
But for very shame I turn my head aside,
While the willows weep beside me, I stroll beside the stream,
That's the place where the old horse died.

He was reaching at his bridle and was going strong and free,
He never seemed to falter or to fail;
. . . Till we crossed the little streamlet in the dell. . . .

'That's as far as I can go,' he wrote.

Charlie Rundle

In January 1958, while fishing in the Darling River near Louth,
New South Wales, John Meredith made friends with Charlie
Rundle, overseer of the Cottage Block, a section of Louth station,
and enjoyed several musical evenings with him in the men's hut
at the shearing shed.

'When You Go to Get Your Shears', which was sung to a version of 'Marching Through Georgia', is similar to a song of Jack
Luscombe's called 'That's How the Shears Go', in that it is a set
of rules rhymed for easy memorizing.

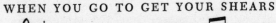

WHEN YOU GO TO GET YOUR SHEARS

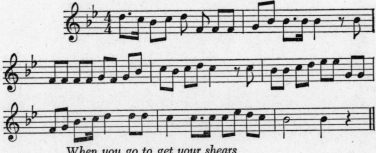

When you go to get your shears
You're not allowed to pick.

The first pair that you collar,
Then it's to that pair you stick.
It is the boss's orders
If you do not like the trick,
You can go somewhere else to look for shearing.

Comparative Source Books

The following publications were consulted in preparing this work. Some items in the list amplify references cited in the text; others contain useful background material.

Anderson, Hugh, *Colonial Ballads*. Melbourne, F. W. Cheshire, 3rd edn 1962.

Anderson, Hugh, *Farewell to Old England*. Adelaide, Rigby Ltd, 1964.

Bell, Robert (ed.), *Ancient Poems, Ballads and Songs of the Peasantry of England*. London, John W. Parker, 1857.

Botsford, F. H. (ed.), *Folk Songs of Many Peoples*. New York, Women's Press, 2 vols, 1921-7.

'Bowyang, Bill', *Australian Bush Recitations*. [Bowen Independent Print, c. 1932-   .]

Broadwood, L. E., and Maitland, J. A. Fuller, *English County Songs*. London, Cramer *et al.*, 1893.

Brown, Max, *Australian Son*. Melbourne, Georgian House, 1948; rev. edn 1956.

Chappell, William, *Popular Music of the Olden Time*. London, Cramer, Beale & Chappell, 2 vols, 1855-9.

Child, F. J. (ed.), *The English and Scottish Popular Ballads*. Boston, Houghton Mifflin, 1904.

Dean-Smith, Margaret, *A Guide to English Folk Song Collections 1822-1952*. Liverpool, University Press, in association with the English Folk Dance and Song Society, 1954.

Fowke, E. F., and Johnston, R. (eds), *Folk Songs of Canada*. Waterloo (Ont.), Waterloo Music Co., 1954.

Gould, S. Baring, and Sheppard, H. Fleetwood, *Songs and Ballads of the West*. London, Patey & Willis, n.d. [4 parts, 1889-92].

Johnson, H. K., *Our Familiar Songs*. New York, Henry Holt, 1909.

Joyce, P. W., *Ancient Irish Music*. 1872.

Joyce, P. W., *Old Irish Folk Music and Songs*. London, Longmans, Green; Dublin, Hodges, Figgis; 1909.

Kidson, Frank, *Traditional Tunes*. Oxford, Chas Taphouse, 1891.

Lloyd, A. L., *The Singing Englishman: an introduction to folksong*. London, Workers' Music Association [1944]. (Keynote Series, Book 4.)

Manifold, John, *The Violin, the Banjo & the Bones: an essay on the instruments of bush music*. Ferntree Gully, Ram Skull Press, 1957. (Black Bull Chapbook no. 6.)

May, Sydney, *The Story of 'Waltzing Matilda'*. Brisbane, W. R. Smith and Paterson, 1944; rev. edn 1955.

Meredith, John, *Songs from the Kelly Country*. [Sydney, Bush Music Club], 1st edn [1955]; 2nd edn [1956].

O Lochlainn, Colm, *Irish Street Ballads*. Dublin, Three Candles; London, Constable [1939].

Palmer, Vance, and Sutherland, Margaret, *Old Australian Bush Ballads*, collected by V. Palmer, music restored by M. Sutherland. Melbourne, Allan [1951].

Paterson, A. B., *Old Bush Songs*. Sydney, Angus & Robertson, 1st edn 1905; 7th edn 1930.

Pizer, M. (ed.), *Freedom on the Wallaby: poems of the Australian people*. Sydney, Pinchgut Press, 1953.

The Queenslanders' New Colonial Camp Fire Song Book, 'by An Old Explorer (or an other man)'. Sydney, F. Cunninghame (printer), 1865.

Sears, Minnie Earl (ed.), assisted by Phyllis Crauford, *Song Index*, Standard Catalog Series. New York, H. W. Wilson Co., 1926; supplement, 1934.

Sharp, Cecil J., *English Folk Songs*, Selected edition. London, Novello & Co., 2 vols [1921].

Sharp, Cecil J., and Marson, Charles L., *Folk Songs from Somerset*, First series. London, Simpkin, Marshall *et al.*, 1904.

Stewart, Douglas, and Keesing, Nancy, *Old Bush Songs and Rhymes of Colonial Times*. Enlarged and revised from the collection of A. B. Paterson. Sydney, Angus & Robertson, 1957.

The Sydney Golden Songster, No. 1. Sydney, W. Hamilton (printer), 1893.

Wells, E. K., *The Ballad Tree: a study of British and American ballads*. London, Methuen, 1950.

Williams, Owen A., *Folk Songs of the Upper Thames*. London, Duckworth, 1923.

T

Index of First Lines

287

Index of Titles

Index of Contributors

*Page numbers in bold type refer to a contributor's own
section in the book*